GW00676327

Forgotten Houses

Holidays in Cornwall
& elsewhere

A guide to manors, houses, cottages and farmhouses available for holidays. Details include scale plans and descriptions of each house including furniture on a sample basis only. This book is produced at irregular intervals and so there will be other houses added after this guide was produced. There may also be deletions, improvements, renovation alterations or changes in detail, layout, furniture and equipment between the date of publication and the time of any holiday.

Please check with the office if you have any queries. We hope all visitors will enjoy their holidays, and that they will find this an interesting and unusual selection of houses.

Forgotten Houses Ltd
01326 340153   www.forgottenhouses.co.uk

Front Cover:
The cover picture shows the spout to the plunge bath built in 1806 at Boconnoc, Lostwithiel.

The Lion Logo:
Our lion is one of six surviving mediaeval lions which, standing proudly on plinths, once formed part of the entrance to a great mansion. They are carved out of moorstone granite, had heraldic shields painted on their chests and may now be some six hundred years old. The National Trust has four of the lions at Trerice and Glendurgan. The other two are at our offices.

This book contains a representative selection of houses available for holidays. It does not necessarily include all houses currently available, and changes in owners' plans may have restricted the availabilty of others. The details provided for each house are believed correct at the time of publication, but most houses will have changes or improvements carried out by owners. We are always happy to answer queries about the houses. Prices are shown on separately printed charts which show the price for each house.

ISBN 978-0-9555511-0-9

Text, Drawings, Plans & Artwork copyright 2007 SCSTyrrell
Published by Pasticcio Ltd   Registered in England No 5125728
Printed by R.Booth Ltd. Penryn Cornwall

Forgotten Houses Ltd
01326 340153   www.forgottenhouses.co.uk

Forgotten Houses are of interest for their setting, architecture or history. Most are listed and in their original setting; one or two are truly unusual. Many have been carefully modernised. However, old houses and old features mean that some are unconventional or do **not** meet modern standards of use or convenience. We believe the historic features and character add to the interest and pleasure of the house, the setting and your holiday.

Most are built of stone with walls two feet thick under slate roofs. Some walls are filled with earth, cob or rab. Nearly all have fire-places or stoves for which wood is supplied within the rental. Televisions & washing machines, as well as books and games, are usually provided.

All provide a good base for holidays from which to go to beaches, moors, cliffs, or places of interest.

House Plans

We have a scale plan for each house. These cannot show all the nooks, crannies or features, but should give an idea of the layout. Because the houses vary in size, each plan is scaled to fit the page and can not be directly compared without use of the scale, which, together with north direction, is marked on each drawing. Furniture and layouts are symbolic only and may vary.

Internet

Our web site has more information than is possible in the handbook. We can also provide panoramic views of the rooms in most houses. The address is at the bottom of this page.

Late News

There is a page on our website for news, details of new houses, last minute reductions and special offers.

Dogs

We accept dogs and pets in nearly all the houses.

The Small Print

Like every other company, our terms and conditions are in this handbook and on the back of our booking form. Please read these and ask if you have any queries.

Prices

Prices for each house are for a full week with no extra charges & no booking fees, save the extras for linen & towels (£5 per person per week) and for pets. There are no meters in any house.

Payment: We need to be paid in the full sterling value for each holiday, by a sterling cheque or sterling order equal to the full sterling price. Every booking needs a booking number, which is usually obtained by phone, followed by sending of a signed booking form and the deposit.

Testimonials and Diaries

Visitors' books are full of stories, drawings and comments on the houses and locality. We like reading your comments, rely on them for testimonials and award occasional prizes for the particularly amusing, interesting or original.

Testimonials are, thankfully, numerous and a small selection is printed towards the back. Of these, the most important are those many who just say:-
"we will be back".

Please Phone Us

Unlike many, we will phone back in the evenings and at weekends. Do phone with questions, or to check availability. We try to give a personal service.

Forgotten Houses Ltd
01326 340153 www.forgottenhouses.co.uk

Forgotten Houses Ltd
01326 340153 www.forgottenhouses.co.uk

Trevoyan House Porch

Forgotten Houses Ltd
01326 340153 www.forgottenhouses.co.uk

Handbook Layout

The houses are shown in rough order of price, size and number of bedrooms.

The first section has a quick run down of the houses, which is then followed by more details for each home including the architectural plans.

Our Web site

The web site has many more pictures than the handbook and also has **panoramic cam-views** which allow you to look round each room and the outside of most houses.

Changeover

The following houses do **not** have Saturday changeovers. Therefore changeovers are on Fridays for:

Barley Crush, Ferryman's, Littleworth, Harry's Court, Grooms, Head Grooms, Treveddoe, Tower House, Bosvarren House, Manorbier Castle

Although bookings are generally for a full week, some houses will accept four day or shorter breaks for dates outside the main holiday seasons.

Making a booking

You will need to get a booking <u>number</u> from us, then fill in a booking form and send the form and a cheque to our offices.

This form is available either on our internet site, (look under "booking form") or on a loose sheet attached to the rate chart sent out with the handbook. The form also has a copy of our terms and conditions.

Please phone or e-mail us to get the booking number, and to check you have all the information you need on any house. Once we have given out the number, we hold the booking for four working days, giving you time to send us the form and a cheque for the deposit or sum due. The address and other details you need are on the booking form.

Prices & Rate Bands

There is a separate loose-leaf rate chart included with the handbook. This shows the name of each house, and the prices for the different weeks or periods. Please phone the office if you have any queries.

Locations

1. Bosvathick Lodge
2. Mellinzeath Farmhouse
3. The Colomiar, Resugga
4. Little Bosvarren
5. Badgers
7. Polwartha Farmhouse
10. The Grooms House
11. Higher Bosvarren Farmhouse
12. Bosbenna
13. Lower Bosvarren Farmhouse
15. Trevoyan
17. Pencobben

21. Tresillian House
27. Little Pinnock Pella
31. Wreckers, Trevoyan
34. Bosvarren House
35. Treveddoe
36. Barley Crush
43. Pennant Farmhouse
47. Josiah's Cottage
48. Long Little Pinnock
49. The Old House Little Pinnock
50. The Gamekeepers House
51. Carew House

53. Swallows, Trevoyan
54. Littleworth
55. The Fish Cellars
57. Dozmary
58. The Tower House
61. Stella Maris, Mousehole
62. Harry's Court, St Ives
63. Waggon House
64. Head Grooms
    Manorbier Castle, South Wales
    Ferryman's, South Wales
    Le Sabotier, Southern France
    Vicinato, Tuscany, Italy

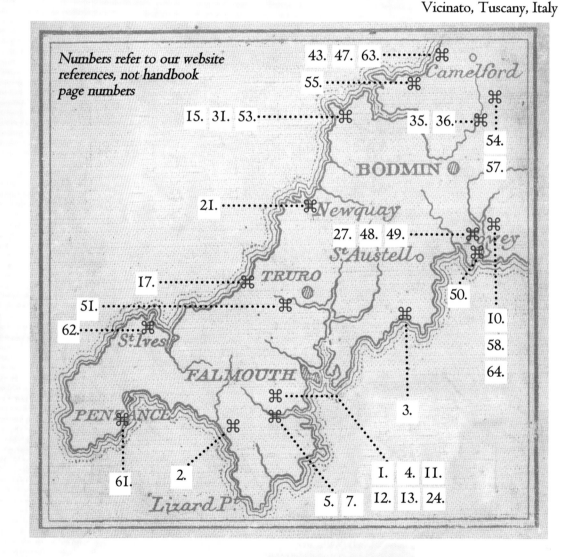

Numbers refer to our website references, not handbook page numbers

A quick guide to the houses

Swallows, Trevoyan, St Merryn   Page 22
Sleeps two & two on sofa bed

Swallows is on the Trevoyan estate between Newquay and Padstow, just inland of the coast. The newly renovated cottage is at one end of an old barn and is on one storey. French windows look east over a small patio and garden area. On the west is a timber and slate decked area together with private lawn looking over other gardens, a large pond and a pergola.

Bosvathick Lodge, Constantine nr Falmouth   Page 24
Sleeps four & cot

Charming granite estate lodge from 1884, listed and retaining its original features. South facing with large garden of lawns and trees set in farmland and woods with good walking. Near riding stables, access to the coast, Helford Estuary and the Lizard. Storage heaters, wood burner and open fire.

Mellinzeath Farmhouse   Page 26
Sleeps four to five

The ultimate romantic lost home. Between Falmouth and Helston, near Helford Estuary. An ancient mill site where the miller's farmhouse was rebuilt in 1665, retains original features including thatched roof, set in secluded wooded valley. Enormous open fireplace. Two bedrooms and bathroom but more basic features than other homes, contributing to unspoilt atmosphere. Romantic, popular, wonderful, but for the more adventurous.

The Colomiar, Resugga   Page 28
Sleeps four to five

In an old farm settlement north of Mevagissey. It has stone walled gardens facing north and south. This listed building retains rag slate roof, stone arched doorways, mullioned windows and traditional feeling. High ceilinged sitting room, a tiny gallery, wood burner, oil fired Rayburn. Close to the Eden Project. A working farm with friendly owners.

Forgotten Houses Ltd
01326 340153 www.forgottenhouses.co.uk

A quick guide to the houses

Josiah's Cottage, Pennant Farm   Page 32
Sleeps four

A stunning listed stone building from 1772, just outside Port Isaac on the north coast and close to beaches and cliffs. Upstairs sitting room looking over fields with original arched beam roof. Renovated winter 2005. Oil central heating. A working farm with great position and views.

Stella Maris   Page 34
Sleeps five

The famous fishing port of Mousehole is beautiful and this granite cottage is in the alley leading to the oldest houses in the village, right by the harbour. Lots to see in Mousehole, Landsend and West Cornwall. Includes 2 beds in attic which provide extra space. Renovated spring 2007. No dogs.

Little Bosvarren   Page 36
Sleeps four to six & cot

West of Falmouth in quiet backwater. Quiet sixteenth century cottage and barn with great granite lintels and quoins. Big sitting room, a big kitchen and walled garden. Wood burning stove and electric radiators. Good walks, views and close to beaches. Fields all around.

Barley Crush   Page 38
Sleeps four to five & cot

On site of Elizabethan farmstead. Large first floor sitting room, & big kitchen in fine renovation. A lovely wooded and pasture valley running up to Bodmin Moor. Comfortable and spacious high ceilinged stone building in beautiful surroundings with good views. Close to Treveddoe. Large renovated barn for wet weather.

For full details and plans see the page for each house

Badgers, Polwartha   Page 42
Sleeps four to six
Badgers is just outside Constantine and near the Helford River. 400 yards from award winning remote pub. Large upstairs sitting room with wood stove, TV. Two bedrooms, (one with double, & one with twin beds). Extra children's loft. Modern bathroom. Oil Rayburn & electric central heating. Ample safe room outside for children.

Polwartha Farmhouse, Constantine   Page 44
Sleeps five
Three bedroom house in country just outside Constantine village & 400 yards from award winning pub. Oil Rayburn, electric heating and open fireplace. Open garden, lawns and fields. Convenient for the Lizard, Falmouth, Helford and cliffs, or beach. Close to Badgers.

Ferryman's, Haverford West   Page 46
Sleeps four.
This beautiful, wide empty estuary had great houses on both sides and a ferryman. The small house is on the water's edge, up the long drive of a private estate. Comfortable, charming, unique, and a fine place of retreat or to explore south west Wales.
Dogs allowed by arrangement.

Fish Cellars, Port Quin   Page 48
Sleeps four to six & cot
Port Quin is a long abandoned fishing cove on the most famous stretch of North Coast between Rock, Polzeath and Port Isaac. Converted fish cellars redecorated 2006. Outstanding position in historic and rare location. Extra bedrooms planned for 2008.

A quick guide to the houses

The Gamekeeper's House, Menabilly, Fowey   Page 52
Sleeps five & cot

It feels really remote, is on one of Cornwall's great stately home estates - but only 500 yards from a beautiful beach & inlet. Renovated in the nineties this is a great forgotten house near Fowey. One of the most popular houses in Cornwall.

Littleworth, and "New House", Bolventor   Page 54
Sleeps four to six, and two extra in cottage can make eight

In a south facing tree'd hollow, Littleworth is remote. High quality renovation and layout. The old cottage with old open fireplace provides extra romantic and unusual private space. High standard and renovation of 2006. Central heating. Ideal retreat on romatic and wild moors but also good touring base. No dogs.

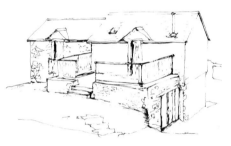

Dozmary, Bodmin Moor   Page 56
Sleeps six

Dozmary Pool is a famous, romantic, remote and beautiful place on the edge of the moor. The house has been rebuilt and beautifully fitted out. Terraces and garden, and the lake right outside. The views are great, there are walks on the moor, and easy access for touring and visiting. Large kitchen, Oil fired heating. Dogs encouraged.

Harry's Court, St Ives   Page 58
Sleeps six

St Ives is justly famous, and this conversion of two old cottages provides delightful space and has balconies over the sandy beach. Small courtyard entrance leads to beautiful little cottage in town centre. New kitchen and works 2007. No dogs. Private parking available. Astonishing position in town and on beach.

Higher Bosvarren Farmhouse, Falmouth   Page 64
Sleeps seven & cot

Traditional C17th farmhouse of thick granite, three bedrooms, dining room & sitting room. Big walk-in fireplaces. Simply and well renovated by conservation experts. Enclosed garden. Good family country house in farmland. Two big wood burning stoves and oil fired central heating. Good for children. Dogs allowed.

For full details and plans see the page for each house

Little Pinnock Pella, Fowey   Page 66
Sleeps four to six

Just north of Fowey, in a small valley of fields and woods, with garden and terrace facing south-west. A high-ceilinged renovation in a mediaeval farm hamlet. Private, spacious, galleried sitting room. Two bedrooms, (gallery has two children's spaces) two bathrooms, modern kitchen, open fireplace, central

The Long Little Pinnock, Fowey   Page 68
Sleeps five to seven

A long stone building, renovated 2004. Long high living room-one end is all window. Two bedrooms each sleeping 2, with 2 more in a bunk room & 2 in gallery. 2 bathroooms. Features include circular wood stair, chicken holes, sheltered garden running to small stream. Oil fired heating. Wood buring stove. Modern kitchen. Fine position near Fowey & beaches.

The Old House, Little Pinnock, Fowey   Page 70
Sleeps six

A genuinely mediaeval house, with great thick walls. Renovated 2004. Upstairs sitting room and big kitchen. 2 open fires. Gardens. Parking. 3 double bedrooms, 2 bathrooms, and sleeping gallery for 2. Oil fired central heating. Wonderful slate roof over stone walls. Close to beaches, to Fowey and to good country.

Wreckers, Trevoyan, St Merryn   Page 74
Sleeps six

Wreckers was the original farmhouse at Trevoyan & has strange twisted stone walls and a great fireplace and stack. It has been carefully restored with a high ceilinged hall and three bedrooms, two bathrooms - sleeping 6. It is not far from Constantine Bay on the north coast, and you can look across the fields to the sea. Gas central heating.

Waggon House, Pennant, Port Isaac   Page 76
Sleeps six to eight

Above Port Isaac, the Waggon house has loads of space and height in old stone buildings of great quality. Renovated in 2007 to keep all features in a simply designed quality refit. Surrounded by fields. Close to coast. Working farm. Spacious for 8 or good for 2. Dogs encouraged. Wonderful north coast base for holidays.

A quick guide to the houses

The Tower House, Boconnoc, Lostwithiel   Page 78
Sleeps four to six, (or more for 2008)

Boconnoc is a private country house with deer park, church and famous gardens. The north wing includes King Charles' room and great views. Newly refitted, quality furniture with more bedrooms planned for 2008. Outstanding, unusual. No dogs.

The Grooms House, Boconnoc, Lostwithiel   Page 80
Sleeps six. Can be combined with Head Grooms to sleep a total of twelve

In stable yard of grand estate, design-winning restoration retains boarded rooms, thick stone walls; many quirky features. Views over church & C18th parkland. Three bedrooms, three bathrooms, high sitting room, central heating. Large park for recreation. Good touring base. Unique historic position. No dogs.

Head Grooms, Boconnoc, Lostwithiel   Page 82
Sleeps six to eight

A bigger house in the stable yard at Boconnoc, reached after a mile of private drive. Very large, high sitting room. Kitchen (new spring 2007) and quirky and interesting interior. Deer park. Fishing in lakes, wonderful smart touring base. Three bedrooms, 3 bathrooms. Dogs allowed by arrangement.

Treveddoe, Warleggan   Page 86
Sleeps seven & cot

An Edwardian farmhouse on the old site of an Elizabethan mansion in beautiful small valley. Lovely remote country south east of Bodmin - half an hour from coast. Big kitchen, breakfast room and sitting room. A romantic location, central for touring. Large garden, woods fields & stream. Close to Barley Crush. Ping pong in Barn. Much revisited. Brilliant location.

Bosbenna, Constantine, Falmouth   Page 88
Sleeps eight & cot

At end of farm drive, old stone buildings around three sides of courtyard. Renovated 2001. Very spacious. Thick walls, high ceilings. Large sitting room, big fireplace, large kitchen. Three bedrooms, two bathrooms plus two beds in attic. Good for children & dogs, three miles from Falmouth beaches. Oil fired central heating. Lots of lawn & open country.

For full details and plans see the page for each house

Lower Bosvarren Farmhouse, Constantine, Falmouth   Page 90
Sleeps eight & cot

Historic Elizabethan farmhouse, four double bedrooms, two sitting rooms, big fireplaces, wood stoves, granite stonework and bread ovens, unusually shaped rooms. Long kitchen. Lots of space outside, garden & grass-covered enclosed yard. Good position for Falmouth, Lizard & SW Cornwall.

Bosvarren House, Constantine, Falmouth   Page 92
Sleeps eight & cot

Fine Georgian country house built 1812, large interesting garden and lawns, in farmland near Falmouth. Unused lower or garden floor. Large drawing room, morning room, dining room, large kitchen (oil fired stove) utility & WC. 4 good bedrooms, one bathroom & one shower room. (Good for dogs). Electric heating, wood burning stoves. Good facilities and area.

Pencobben, Godrevy Point, North Coast   Page 96
Sleeps nine

The north coast at Godrevy has dramatic scenery and is close to sandy beaches of St Ives Bay. Rebuilt house with spectacular views and surroundings over National Trust owned headland. Towans & dunes, isolated location, enclosed gardens, gas central heating. Walk to secluded beach. Designed for family holidays but also suitable for one or two. Fine for dogs.

Trevoyan, St Merryn, Padstow   Page 98
Sleeps eleven

Fine old listed farmhouse on north coast near many popular beaches. Lawns and gravel drive. Five bedrooms, two bathrooms, four poster bed, two sitting rooms. Modern kitchen units, electric oven & hobs and coal Rayburn. Wonderful old house in first class position for beaches on North Coast. (Can be taken with Wreckers for larger groups).

Forgotten Houses Ltd
01326 340153   www.forgottenhouses.co.uk

A quick guide to the houses

Carew House, St Day
Sleeps ten & cot

An extraordinary Regency country house hidden behind a small cottage in the lovely village of St Day not far from the North Coast. Large rooms, modern kitchen, recently renovated, lots of space and style, fine decor and furniture. High walled large garden. Oil fired heating and loads of features and assets. Close to such good beaches as Portreath and Porthtowan.

Pennant Farmhouse, Port Isaac, North Coast
Sleeps twelve

Large eighteenth century farmhouse just outside Port Isaac, with good views of coast. Five bedrooms, two big reception rooms, hall & 38 foot long kitchen. Refitted in 2003/4. Oil fired Aga. Big garden. In an outstanding position - close to good beaches and coastal walks and it is such an interesting house.

Tresillian House, Newquay
Sleeps fifteen & cot

Substantial Regency country house in 200 acres about 5 miles from Newquay and coast. Luxurious quality, renovated and decorated again in 2007, retaining many features with central heating, Aga, drawing room (with Carrera marble fireplace), fine library, terrace, large walled garden with pond and plenty of lawn. An outstanding country house in a good location. No dogs.

Manorbier Castle, Pembrokeshire, South Wales
Sleeps twelve & cot

Within the walls of this great mediaeval castle is a house built of and within the battlements. Your keys are those of the castle. The house has good rooms and furniture and four bathrooms. The layout includes 13th century rooms, large sitting room, narrow stairs, a modern kitchen, walled garden and a chalet to provide some of the bed space. The beach is 100 yards away. This is one of the great holiday homes in Britain. An astonishing, comfortable house which is also one of Wales' most famous castles.
Dogs allowed out of season only.

Forgotten Houses Ltd
01326 340153   www.forgottenhouses.co.uk

For full details and plans see the page for each house

Le Sabotier, Montcuq, Lot et Garonne, France   Page 110
Sleeps four to six
South of Dordogne, renovated by English owner (who is nearby to help), two bedrooms, one with balcony. Futon in sitting room. Two bathrooms. Bare stone walls, high ceilings, wood burning stove. Shared <u>swimming pool</u>. Rural pleasures of sunflowers, vines and good wines. Rolling countryside rich in fortified hill towns, castles, caves and gorges.

Vicinato, Garfagnana, Tuscany, Italy   Page 112
Sleeps eight
Fine old 18th century Tuscan stone farmhouse in Forgotten Houses style with good views, covered terrace, washing machine, modern cooker, fireplace, wanderable vineyards, fruit & olive trees. Enormous open terrace. More rooms and bathrooms being added through renovation. Public swimming pool at bottom of hill.

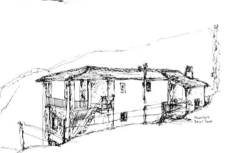

The following houses do **not** have Saturday changeovers:

Barley Crush, Ferryman's, Littleworth, Harry's Court, Grooms, Head Grooms, Treveddoe, Tower House, Bosvarren House, Manorbier Castle   *as at date of printing*

Low tide view from Ferryman's

View from Littleworth

Forgotten Houses Ltd
01326 340153   www.forgottenhouses.co.uk

Forgotten Houses Ltd
01326 340153 www.forgottenhouses.co.uk

Swallows

Bosvathick Lodge

Forgotten Houses Ltd
01326 340153 www.forgottenhouses.co.uk

Mellinzeath

Colomiar

Forgotten Houses Ltd

01326 340153   www.forgottenhouses.co.uk

Swallows, Trevoyan

St Merryn 69

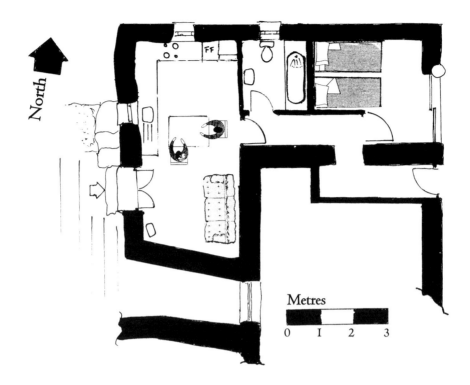

Swallows is at one end of barns built in the 18th century. The north range has a lovely burnt sienna lichen covered slate roof. The cottage is built partly of slatey stone, some slate hanging, part slate & part lead roof, and is on a single storey. The entire building is attached to the northern end of North Barn. The owners live in that wing to the immediate south of Swallows.

The entrance on the east is by a stable door into a corridor with exposed stone walls. On the right is then a bedroom fitted with a pair of beds which can be joined. Large double glazed french windows look east over a timbered patio and garden area with walls, pavements, bench, Buddha. Behind the bedroom is a bathroom, with floor of slate tiles, some exposed wall and a 6ft Jacuzzi bath with a shower attachment. The sitting room has french windows to the garden the other side, looks south west and has exposed stone slate walls, country dresser, books & timbered ceiling with down lights. Large TV with DVD. Beyond the dining table is a fitted kitchen with washing machine, tumble drier, microwave, fridge/freezer and gas boiler. The floor is carpeted. The windows are double glazed. There is a sofa bed to allow an extra two people to sleep in the sitting room.

On the west is a timber paved and slate decked area and a wall around the house looking over other gardens together with private areas of lawn looking over a large pond with much statuary and a cast iron pergola. Lots of lawn outside and private parking. Dogs Allowed.

Sleeps 2 plus 2 on sofa bed

Forgotten Houses Ltd
01326 340153 www.forgottenhouses.co.uk

Swallows, Trevoyan

Swallows is between Newquay and Padstow and just inland of the coast between Porthcothnan Bay and St Merryn. At the seaward end of an old farmstead, you can see across the fields to Treyarnon Bay. The nearest beach is walkable, down the hill to the west. There are many sandy beaches close by- the parish of St Merryn claims one for each day of the week. There is also good surfing and smaller beaches below the cliffs. This area has plenty of facilities and activities but is also a good place to base a touring holiday of the area.

Trevoyan is an old listed farmstead, with a scatter of lovely weathered grey and brown stone buildings under large rag slate roofs. The large eighteenth century barns are still part barn and part accommodation with the owner living in one wing. Swallows is a new renovation at the end of the building. Trevoyan and Wreckers, which are separately described, together with the old barns and gardens, form a magnificent backdrop for Swallows. All are owned by the same couple. Swallows has private parking right by the front door, and there is a small private garden to three sides. There is a larger area of garden and ornamented horse pond and loggia just beyond this with views of the fields on all sides. North of the house is a large buttercup pasture in which cows are grazing and from which you can see clear to Treyarnon bay and beyond. Trevoyan is a private house and farmstead in a private and lovely country setting, which is also at the heart of one of the most popular areas of Cornwall.

Forgotten Houses Ltd
01326 340153 www.forgottenhouses.co.uk

Bosvathick Lodge

Falmouth 25

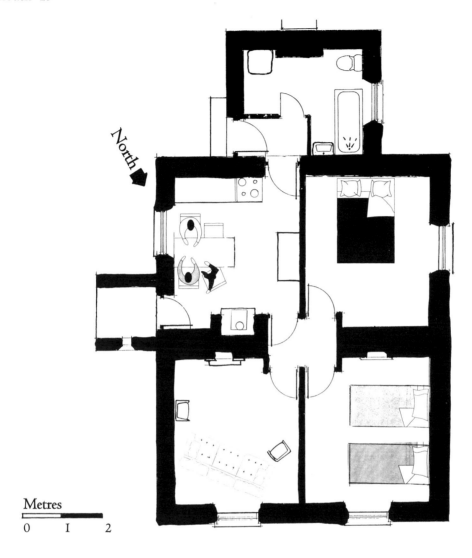

Metres

0   I   2

The Lodge has a small kitchen, with table, chairs and a granite fireplace with woodburning stove. The kitchen has electric cooker, fridge & microwave. The sitting room has an open grate and television. One bedroom has a large double bed and the other twin beds. Through a hall from the kitchen is the modern bathroom, which includes a power shower fitted over the bath. There is also a washing machine. Heating is by electric night storage radiators and the wood burner. Electricity and wood are included in the rent.

The house was redecorated in spring 2005 by designers *Josephine*.

The rooms have high ceilings, but the house is cosy. There is safe off road parking within the large garden, which is a mixture of trees and lawns. Well fenced in for dogs, it is therefore, a reasonably safe garden for small children who may also, with supervision, enjoy the tree house in one corner. **Sleeps 4 & cot**

Forgotten Houses Ltd
01326 340153 www.forgottenhouses.co.uk

Bosvathick Lodge
Falmouth 25

Bosvathick was a farming hamlet in the hilly farmland just inland from Falmouth. In 1760 it became the centre of a traditional estate & in 1884 the owners added a pretty lodge to one side of their main entrance, with its magnificent lions and balled piers.

The Lodge (for which the first & only sketch was on the back of a now treasured envelope) was designed to be quaint. It was built for £210 of granite ashlar, with a pyramidal hipped roof of fish scale slate with deep eaves, decorated ridges and barges, a gabled porch and fine chimneys. The house is listed, and has been kept with its original features. The Lodge is charming. It has its own little drive, lawn and large garden with many trees on the south, with farmland beyond the garden. Across the road above the high Cornish stone banks is more farmland, a tree lined drive leading to tracks, wood & farmland where visitors are welcome to walk. A couple of fields away are horse riding stables. There is access to the coast, Helford Estuary and the Lizard. The house is in beautiful countryside, in a maze of tiny lanes, and only a couple of miles from the coast. There is a prize-winning pub not far away and it is well placed for beaches (including three at Falmouth) and the area's attractions, restaurants, & activities. Several visitors have said the house is much nicer than a handbook can describe.

Forgotten Houses Ltd
01326 340153   www.forgottenhouses.co.uk

Mellinzeath

Helford River 10

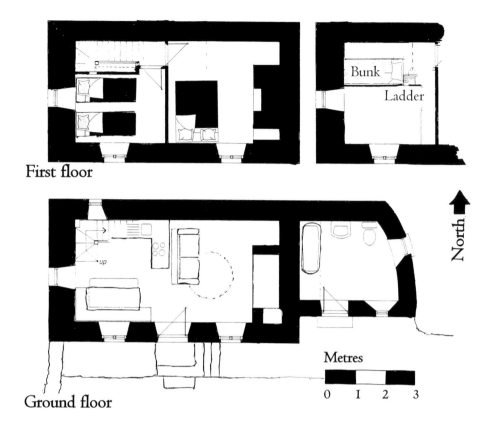

First floor

Bunk
Ladder

North

Ground floor

Metres

0   1   2   3

Mellinzeath has a sitting room combined with kitchen, & two bedrooms & bathroom. The second bedroom has a high bunk for a third child. The timber kitchen is basic but has built in cooker & hob, modern fridge, fitted table & benches. Downstairs the floors are the original rough granite or slate & upstairs wide timber floors, both with rugs. There are large open wood fires for heat and electric radiators upstairs.   The refitted bathroom is in an outside wing with a roll top bath on splendid feet, and a secondary hip bath for the adventurous. The water is heated by electric immersion. Free wood & mains electricity.   No TV reception, no washing machine, no freezer.

Fifteen acres of wooded valley and noisy streams; local walking permitted. You are met in the village & led to the car park in the farmyard. You and your luggage are both delivered and picked up from the house, other times it's a 660 metre walk from your car. It is for the more adventurous, with fewer facilities than most, but loved by children, young couples, honey-mooners, grandparents & those seeking quiet. The adjoining barn has been rebuilt as a wood store on the ground floor and for play, contemplation or camping on the first floor with good lighting and shutters. Bring Rubber Boots. Ideal for dogs.

Sleeps 4/5

Forgotten Houses Ltd
01326 340153   www.forgottenhouses.co.uk

Mellinzeath

Helford River 10

Mellinzeath was once the farmhouse of the miller in this wooded valley which has a thousand years of recorded history. Thought to have been rebuilt after a fire in 1665, it has been little altered since - a really forgotten although renovated house. It retains its original size, thick granite walls and many features. We think the valley is quite extraordinarily lovely, with a tiny meadow, streams of fast rushing water, total seclusion & privacy, shelter from the wind, facing south with meadow, streams, hillside and woodland to explore. The house is thatched.

In the floor is set a worn millstone; there are two fireplaces, a bread oven, a winding stair to a high trussed romantic roof. The bathroom, in an extension alongside, has an arched door and mediaeval windows reused from an older house. Outside, there are stone walls, a granite barn, streams & spring. Past a lawn sloping down to the south there is a long shallow pond and plenty of shallow streams for children to play in. You can walk round the hillsides - and also to a good pub.

This is perhaps our most popular house, but you need a spirit of adventure. Although many visitors never leave the house, garden, water and woods, Mellinzeath is in the prime Helford River area, close to every facility of Falmouth, the Helford Estuary and Lizard Peninsula.

Forgotten Houses Ltd
01326 340153 www.forgottenhouses.co.uk

The Colomiar

Resugga, St Stephens 20

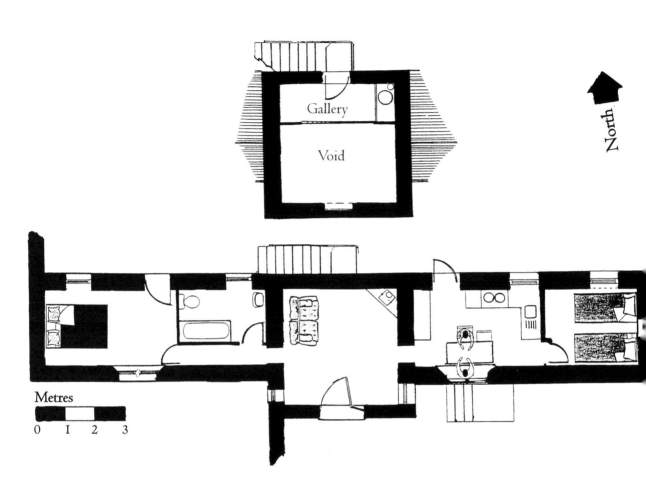

The Colomiar is a beautiful small house with big features and lots of architectural interest. It has a random rag slate roof, fine stonework and mullions, oak framed mullion windows, granite walls and two stone arch doorways.

The roof-high sitting room has a tiny gallery, wood burner, TV & a sofa bed. Two bedrooms and one bathroom. The country style kitchen includes Rayburn & microwave and there is always warmth from the oil fired Rayburn. There are also electric radiators and the wood burner. There is a detached utility room with washing machine and drier & freezer. Electricity and wood are included in the rent. There is good parking, a safe north garden walled right round - good for small children - a walled south facing garden and plenty of space on the estate to wander. Barbecue. Dogs usually allowed. **Sleeps 4**

The Colomiar

Resugga, St Stephens 20

Resugga is one of the older farm settlements in the country 5 miles north of Mevagissey, west of St Austell, 11 miles from Newquay and 3 miles from Heligan. It is a fine collection of old buildings and good Tudor stone work and shares its name with the Celtic hill fort nearby.

In 1283, Michael de Rosugo had to flee after he'd slain his friend with a dagger. Recent occupiers have been more respectable citizens and continued to improve the house. In the eighteenth century the farmer built a fine stable for his own cob, with mounting block, a loft above, barns to each side and a gabled pigeon house, all with thick granite walls and random slate roofs. The front door has fine curved granite quoins and was big enough for a horse and rider. The building faces south and has stone walled gardens both north & south. This is now an enchanting and interesting house, retaining all the features that have made it a listed building. The central section has a high roofed sitting room and eccentric gallery, with the wings providing bedrooms, kitchen and bathroom. There is a walled garden to the north, safe for the smallest children. The Colomiar is up a long paved farm drive and it is easy to get to the famous coast just south, to which it is said there was once an old smugglers route.

The farmers live next door and are happy to show children the animals and the walks around the farm. The visitors' book is full of admiration and pleasure at the house, its surroundings and the friendly reception. The house is in green country but convenient to visit the coast and beaches, Newquay, Heligan, The Eden Project, Charlestown, …indeed The Colomiar is well placed.

Forgotten Houses Ltd
01326 340153 www.forgottenhouses.co.uk

Josiah's

Little Bosvarren

Forgotten Houses Ltd
01326 340153   www.forgottenhouses.co.uk

Barley Crush

Forgotten Houses Ltd
01326 340153 www.forgottenhouses.co.uk

Josiah's, Pennant Farm

Port Isaac, North Cornwall 66

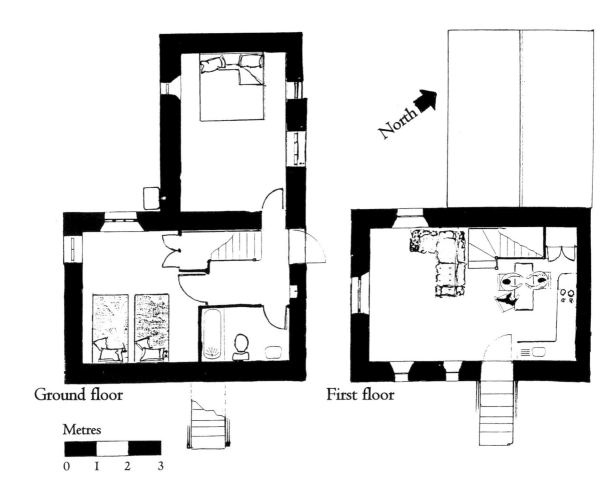

Ground floor

Metres

0   1   2   3

First floor

Josiah's Cottage has thick stone walls, narrow windows, with reused tudor stone under a double hipped great rag and scantle slate roof. Two bedrooms, one bathroom (shower over bath). The ground floor door leads to a small hall. The main entrance is up old steps to a large living room on first floor with high open roof, & curved braces from the 1772 rebuild. TV; DVD and CD Player. The small kitchen at one end of the living room has new units, electric oven & hob, microwave, dishwasher, fridge & washer/dryer.

The decoration is plain & simple. Wood floor to first floor. Light green carpets downstairs. Vinyl in bathroom. Oil fired central heating. Sitting room has 4 windows, looking over farmland. Long drive with good views of coast leads to house with walled/fenced garden & own parking off old farm yard. Garden furniture. Good brick barbecue. Renovated 05/06 Dogs allowed.

Sleeps 4

Forgotten Houses Ltd
01326 340153   www.forgottenhouses.co.uk

Josiah's, Pennant Farm

Port Isaac, North Cornwall 66

Pennant Farm has always been an important site at the head of the small valley that runs in from the fishing village at Port Isaac on the north coast of Cornwall. Port Isaac was chosen as the setting for a current TV serial because of the beauty and interest of the seaside village, cliffs, scenery and beaches of Cornwall. There was once a great mediaeval farmstead at Pennant, which moved up hill, with replacement 18th century farm buildings.

Josiah's Cottage was built in 1772 (the date is low on one corner) with stones and timber from earlier buildings to an ordered design by a landowner wishing to show his improving status. He did a good job and made a lovely little building. Rows of pigeon holes for winter food are set around the top within thick walls, under a grand slate roof. The building was later extended by a wing to the north and is now at the west end of a lane with six separate old buildings and a small horse pond. The main farm has moved away to the east and the working farm is separated from the row of old buildings. The owners live on the site.

The Port Isaac area is one of the most popular places in Cornwall. There is plenty to do on the cliffs, and on the beaches, either at small sandy coves or the more well known ones like Polzeath. There are bistros, restaurants, good pubs and a sense of history, place and community. There is lots to do elsewhere but the house is also a comfortable and intriguing retreat.

Forgotten Houses Ltd
01326 340153 www.forgottenhouses.co.uk

Stella Maris

Mousehole 78

Stella Maris is in a small alley leading to the harbour. The front is built of large granite blocks with good sized windows and is only a few yards from the village centre.

The front door opens off the street into a large room with the sitting room to the right. This has comfortable sofas, working fireplace, window seats and quirky cupboards. At the other end is the newly designed and refitted kitchen (spring 2007).

This has electric oven & hob, washing machine, dishwasher, microwave and fridge freezer. There is a breakfast table in the window.

Upstairs are two bedrooms, a charming double bedded room at one end and a good sized single room at the other. The small bathroom is between the bedrooms and newly refitted (spring 2007) with a shower (no bath). A steep companion style ladder leads up to the open plan attic where two built in beds provide overflow accommodation.

The whole house is newly carpeted and decorated in careful and simple colours and is comfortable and well thought out. Electric heating. No parking at the house, although it is available close by. No Dogs.

Sleeps 3 to 5

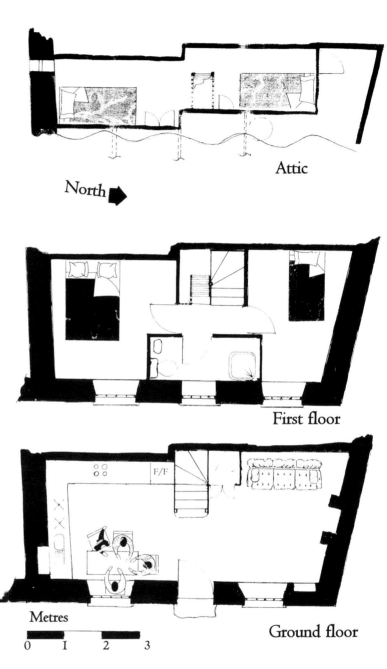

Attic

North

First floor

Metres

0 1 2 3

Ground floor

Forgotten Houses Ltd
01326 340153 www.forgottenhouses.co.uk

Stella Maris

Mousehole 78

Mousehole is beyond Newlyn and Penzance in the far west of Cornwall and is famous for the small harbour cut into the cliff. The village is built up the steep sides of the cove with many narrow streets and alleys. In addition to being one of the most picturesque harbours and villages in Cornwall, it also has good pubs, small restaurants art galleries and shops. The little granite houses and fishermen's cottages make a lovely and deservedly popular place to visit.

The port continues to be a fishing base, although also the home of artists. Mousehole was burnt by the Spanish four hundred years ago. Resistance was led from an old house close to Stella Maris which is itself of granite rebuilt in the nineteenth century and is only a few yards from the sandy beach within the harbour walls. Staying in Mousehole is so interesting and restful. On trips out, you can walk the coastal path, or tour the cliffs towards Lands End. It is not far to visit the whole south west from St Michael's Mount to the Tate Gallery, to go surfing, or swim off the fine sandy beaches of St Ives bay.   Stella Maris is a comfortable, newly refurbished and relaxing little house.

Forgotten Houses Ltd
01326 340153 www.forgottenhouses.co.uk

Little Bosvarren

Constantine, Falmouth 17

Little Bosvarren is spacious and has been well and carefully renovated. Decoration is simple, with plain walls and carpet and inset light fittings. The large kitchen (with built in units, fridge, microwave, electric oven & hob and a breakfast table) is half way up between sitting room and bedrooms. The stair has fine joinery.

The very long sitting room is upstairs & has high ceilings & a wood burner. There are two bedrooms and one bathroom. The bathroom also has a wet room style shower in the corner. The utility room has a washing machine, W.C. and basin.

All rooms are carpeted (new 2005/6) save the bathroom (terracotta tiles) and kitchen (vinyl 2004).

Two additional collapsible beds may be available for children. Cot and high chair available. Electric heating. BBQ in garden shed.

Interesting and enclosed lawned garden. which is walled right round and good for small children.
There are plenty of walks around the farm and estate. There is safe private parking. Dogs allowed.

Sleeps 4-6 & Cot

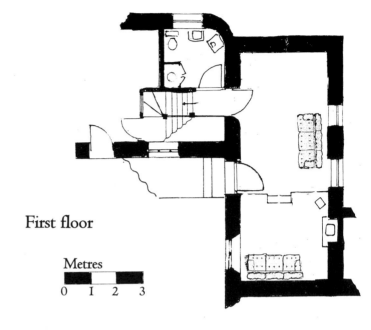

First floor

Metres

0 1 2 3

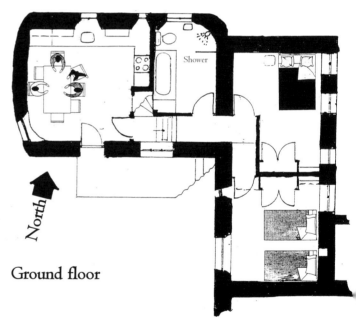

North

Ground floor

Little Bosvarren

Constantine, Falmouth 17

Little Bosvarren is a lovely old stone cottage with lots of interesting features in unspoilt countryside. Bosvarren is a hamlet of five houses up a tree lined drive some four miles from Falmouth. The site has been a collection of farms since the twelfth century and is now a quiet backwater including two Elizabethan farmhouses & a larger Georgian house. All the houses are of granite two feet thick with great lintels and quoins.

Little Bosvarren was a 1990 renovation of a sixteenth century cottage and later stone barn. There is an enormous upstairs sitting room, with wood burning stove, a platformed floor and high ceiling. The slope of the land and the old cobbled ramp allow the first floor direct access to the walled garden. The changing levels provide an interesting, spacious house. The old cottage has rounded corners, a hidden cobbled floor, (now under timber), curious windows and a large kitchen at 'half' level, which also has a door to the garden. The staircase is light and pleasant with massive timber newels. The two bedrooms downstairs each have a big cupboard.

The house is in green, quiet and beautiful countryside. It is just over 3 miles from the coast and well placed for the beaches, facilities, restaurants and the activities of the South West, with Falmouth, Helston, the Lizard & the North Coast at St Agnes all within half an hour's drive. A famous pub and riding stables are close by. There are good walks round the farm, and fields right by the house.

Forgotten Houses Ltd
01326 340153   www.forgottenhouses.co.uk

Barley Crush

Warleggan Bodmin 54

The Barley Crush is an upside down house with large sitting room upstairs. From the walled garden a glazed door opens into the large kitchen-breakfast room, which is a joy. It has dishwasher, electric cooker, microwave, fridge/freezer, high chair, and everything else you could need, leaving a great space for the farmhouse table and chairs. The main hall is a step up and has boiler, washing machine, tumble dryer, cupboard for coats & boots, and a porch outside. The open stairs are gated top and bottom, & lead to the large upstairs sitting room, which has exposed beams, TV and video, payphone and a wood-burning stove. Another glazed door opens from the sitting room onto old stone steps down to the garden.

One bedroom with kingsize bed and its own bathroom is upstairs under sloping ceilings, the other is downstairs, also with bathroom. This bedroom has a third full size bed if needed. The downstairs table can seat more so that, if let with Treveddoe next door, larger groups can eat here.

Games room in barn across the lane. Walking around farm allowed. Oil-fired Central Heating, double glazing. Wood for the fire is supplied. Natural spring water supply.

The surrounding fields have cattle and sheep but controlled dogs are allowed. High Chair.

Friday Changeover   Sleeps 4-5 & Cot

First flo

Shower over bath

Plus Roller bed under

Metres

0   1   2   3

North

Ground fl

Barley Crush

BARLEYCRUSH.

South and south east of Bodmin is a wild, pastoral, beautiful and little known land. The Barley Crush is at Treveddoe Farm half way down a green cul-de-sac valley to the south of Bodmin moor. The Barley Crush looks over the pastures and woodland of the farm & was a barn probably rebuilt in the 19th century, until converted in 2001. The house is beautifully and simply fitted out, with an upstairs sitting room, a second outside stair, an enclosed walled garden, a games barn and many quirky features. It has central heating. It was intended, with Treveddoe, to let the owners' large family all get together, so can be taken with Treveddoe Farmhouse some 40

yards away, to sleep up to 12. The house is in a tranquil setting & feels a long way from anywhere, although only ten minutes from more well known areas. It is ideal for walkers and those who want to get away from it all and also has direct access onto the Moor.

The river Warleggan tumbles along its southern boundary. There are good walks through the semi-ancient woodland, with beautiful wild flowers in the spring. This is a good base for exploring Cornwall but it's always lovely to get back to the farm after a day out. The nearest good country pub is a couple of miles east, and you can walk to the beautiful village church of Warleggan.

Forgotten Houses Ltd
01326 340153 www.forgottenhouses.co.uk

Badgers

Polwartha

Ferryman's

The Fish Cellars

Forgotten Houses Ltd

01326 340153   www.forgottenhouses.co.uk

Badgers

Constantine Falmouth 21

Badgers is comfortable, well insulated & has visitors back again and again. The porch has a fine stained glass badger window. The kitchen has terracotta tiles and the remaining ground floor rooms are newly carpeted. The first floor is boarded and covered with rugs. The sitting room upstairs has plenty of light, views, a stone fireplace & wood burning stove, TV, CD player & radio. There are two bedrooms, one double one twin and a gallery loft with two beds reached by a steep ladder from the sitting room, suitable for adventurous children.

There is a small stained glass window in the attic. The bathroom has bath & shower over the bath. The kitchen is long and high with good wooden units, a dining table at one end & a stone corner seat. The kitchen is heated by an oil fired Rayburn and range cooker. There is also a small electric cooker, microwave, dishwasher, and fridge with small freezer section. The utility is in an outhouse with washing machine, tumble drier and a further W.C. together with a games room with pool table. There are lawns on both sides of the house, ample parking, safe play for children and acres of land around the house. BBQ outside. The house has electric heaters to supplement the Rayburn and wood burning stove for which there is plenty of fuel. Dogs welcome.

Sleeps 4/6

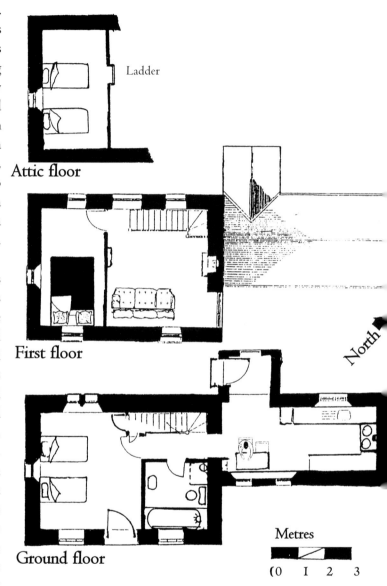

Ladder

Attic floor

First floor

North

Ground floor

Metres

(0 1 2 3

Badgers

Constantine Falmouth 21

Badgers is just outside Constantine, some five miles west of Falmouth. It's about half a mile from the Helford Estuary and some 400 yards from a country pub which has recently won three awards as the nicest in Britain. Not only are the surroundings picturesque, with access along winding "up and downy" lanes, but Badgers is in one of the best areas for facilities, beaches, the coast and country. The adjoining lane on the line of an old Roman road crosses two old granite bridges, one last rebuilt in 1572 for the sum of £6.13s.4d.

Badgers is about 80 yards from Polwartha,

in the old farmstead which is one of the older sites in the parish, at the head of the network of creeks leading to the sea. The site is just below the crest of a hill with views over the steep wooded valleys to each side and the tree lined green lanes. Badgers is off a hard farm track.

Originally built of granite and slate around 1860, it has now been renovated retaining old features. There are oak framed iron windows, window seats, openings and high timber trussed ceilings to the sitting room. There's a sunny terrace facing SW in the partly walled garden and plenty of space for outdoor games.

Forgotten Houses Ltd
01326 340153   www.forgottenhouses.co.uk

Polwartha Farmhouse

Constantine Falmouth 13

Polwartha is comfortable, fully carpeted and regularly renovated. Downstairs the large sitting room stretches along one side of the house with open fireplace, TV and video.

Beyond the dining room, the kitchen has dishwasher, modern units, oil fired Rayburn, a gas hob, microwave, fridge with small freezer section & small electric cooker to supplement the range cooker.

Upstairs are three bedrooms, a 5ft double bed, one with twin beds and a charming single, (the goose room) together with a fully tiled modern bathroom (renovated 2004). Power shower over bath. Washing machine. A second separate WC is upstairs.

A second washing machine with tumble drier is in a utility about 50 yards away, with a further W.C. and games room with pool table.   The house has telephone for incoming calls only.

There are lawns on both sides of the house, ample parking in the old farmyard and six acres of land (and perhaps some cattle) with the house. Barbecue. There are good views of the countryside.   The house has electric central heating to supplement the Rayburn and open fire for which there is plenty of wood. Dogs welcome.

Sleeps 5

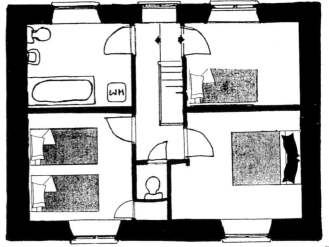

First floor

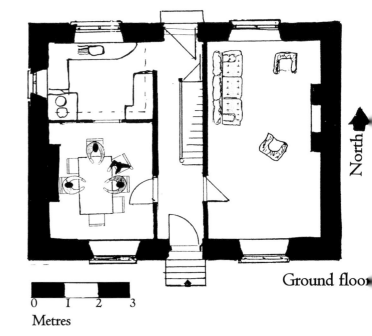

North

Ground floor

0 1 2 3

Metres

Polwartha Farmhouse

Constantine, Falmouth 13

Polwartha is with Badgers, just outside Constantine in famously attractive countryside, some five miles west of Falmouth. It's about half a mile from the Helford Estuary, and 400 yards from a country pub which has recently won three awards as the nicest in Britain. Not only are the surroundings picturesque, with access along winding "up and downy" lanes, but Polwartha is not far from many attractions and beaches. The adjoining lane on the line of an old Roman road crosses two old granite bridges, one last rebuilt in 1572 for the sum of £6.13s.4d.

Polwartha was one of the oldest farming sites in the parish, at the head of the network of creeks leading to the sea. The site is just below the crest of a hill with views over the steep wooded valleys to each side and the old tree lined green lane that used to be the main road south west leading down to the valley. The house, off a hard track from the road, is a handsome upright square house erected around 1910 with granite walls two feet thick, perhaps with some of the stone from the old house. Inside, the sitting room has a granite fireplace for wood and coal.

Outside, there are lawns on two sides, a meadow to one side & out-buildings & Badgers about 80 yards away. There is plenty of garden and space for games.

Forgotten Houses Ltd
01326 340153 www.forgottenhouses.co.uk

Ferryman's

Slebech Park, Pembrokeshire   75

Ferryman's Cottage is comfortable and has been simply decorated. The small hall leads to the kitchen which looks along the yew tree walk below the terraced gardens of Slebech. The kitchen has microwave, low fridge, dishwasher, electric hob and stove. The bathroom with airing cupboard is also off the hall and has a power shower over the bath

The sitting room has comfortable sofa & armchair, Welsh Dresser, and a fine mid Victorian working fireplace. The floor has the original black and red tiles with rugs. The table in the window looks over the lake. Flat screen TV & CD player.

The two south facing bedrooms, which are reached from a slate floored corridor, have windows looking down the estuary. The double bedroom keeps the old hob grate, filled with pinecones, between the original deep cupboards. The second bedroom has another hob grate and blue painted wide plank floors with rugs, antique furniture and twin beds.

Steep stone stairs go down to the utility room with chest freezer, oil fired boiler, drying facilities and unused kitchen range. More steps then go through the lean-to down to the fore-shore. Here is a large grassy play area, and garden furniture but the deep water is not far away. Three times a month the water comes right up to the steps.

Ferryman's is private and set between the sea and the formal gardens. Although only a few hundred yards from other buildings, it feels remote. There is plenty of space to walk and wander. Private parking is a short walk from the house. Oil-fired central heating. Laundry room in stable yard. Free wood. Barbecue. Dogs welcome by arrangement.

Friday Changeover   Sleeps 4

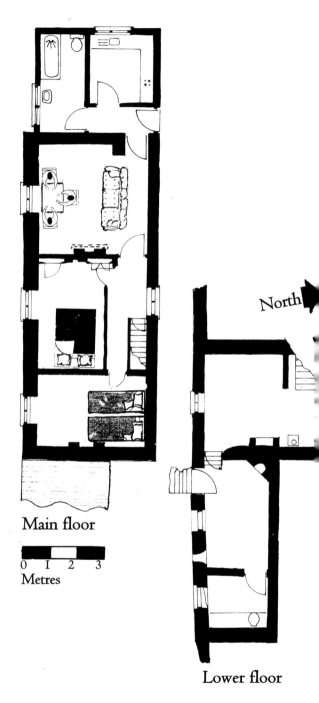

North

Main floor

0   1   2   3
Metres

Lower floor

Ferryman's

Pembrokeshire has castles, small towns, old buildings. There are also 275 miles of coastal path past cliffs and sandy beaches. Ferryman's is in the Daucleddau Estuary, a maritime park of dramatic scenery and a sanctuary for wading birds, otters and seals. Ten miles from Pembroke, a small town with magnificent castle, the empty estuary remains wide at Slebech. Here was a crossing point, commandery, hospitalry, and mediaeval religious house helping pilgrims on their way.

Ferryman's, on an ancient site, is built of stone and 18th century brick at the waters edge. Behind the house are the gardens of Slebech Hall. The drive is about 1.5 miles long. After you pass the big house, stables, Holy Island and a ruined church, you park the car and walk the last yards along the water's edge .

The countryside is stunning, wild and of sweeping landscape. From the windows one looks south across an empty estuary lined by oaks. The setting for this house is incomparable.

Locally, there is lots to see and do, including castle visits, fine eating, a tour of the tiny cathedral city of St Davids or visits to cliff or beach. Local sports include golf, cycling, canoeing.

The house is a comfortable and relaxing retreat. Though you may not wish to leave Slebech, it is ideally placed for touring around Pembrokeshire.

The Fish Cellars

Port Quin, North Cornwall 76

The Fish Cellars is in the section of building nearest to the sea. The entrance is at first floor level up the hill behind the house There are old and unoccupied cellars on the ground floor. The whole house has been redecorated in plain colours and fitted with new plain carpets in 2006. All windows are double glazed.

The large sitting room takes up one end of the building. There is a fireplace and working grate. TV and DVD player. Good views from the windows. The kitchen has modern units, inset electric cooker and hob (new 2006), washing machine, microwave, fridge. The corridor leads past the bathroom, which also has a power shower, to two bedrooms. The first has two new single beds and the second has a double bed and futon. Both bedrooms have views down the old harbour. Oil fired central heating.

An extra floor of accommodation is to be fitted out during the winter of 2007/8. This will provide extra space, bedrooms and bathrooms for 2008.

Just behind the buildings at the start of the valley is a large area of private rough garden and field with a small patio area and clothes drying line. Barbecue. No mobile telephone or radio reception. Dogs are welcome.

Sleeps 4-6 and may be more

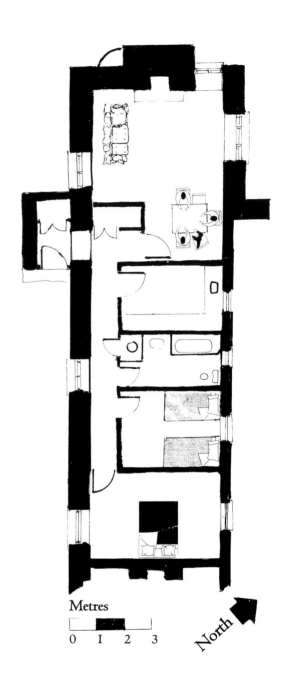

Metres

0   1   2   3

North

Forgotten Houses Ltd
01326 340153   www.forgottenhouses.co.uk

The Fish Cellars

Just beyond the famous north coast beaches around Polzeath is one of the finest stretches of cliff, cove and beaches in Cornwall. Once there were several small fishing villages using the deep fjord like inlets for shelter. However, legend says that the whole fleet of Port Quin perished in a storm and so the village has been derelict for 150 years.

If you look hard beneath the greenery there are still remnants of the houses along the hill. Now at the end of a sheltered green valley with high cliffs to either side are only two houses lived in all year round, and some National Trust cottages. Much of the rest, including the Fish Cellars, has been owned by the same family for over a century. The high walled courtyard buildings of the Fish Cellars were for drying nets and pressing and salting sardines.

The narrow coast road winds through from Port Isaac, past the house and on to the point. The scenery is breathtaking, The house is only ten yards or so from the long rocky much photographed beach and inlet. You can walk for miles along the cliffs beside the sea.

This must be one of the most romantic spots in Cornwall, right on the beach but yet it's close to the sights and sports of a well provided and interesting holiday area.

Forgotten Houses Ltd

01326 340153   www.forgottenhouses.co.uk

The Gamekeeper's House

Littleworth

Forgotten Houses Ltd
01326 340153   www.forgottenhouses.co.uk

Dozmary Pool

Harry's Court

Forgotten Houses Ltd
01326 340153 www.forgottenhouses.co.uk

The Gamekeeper's House

Menabilly, Fowey 64

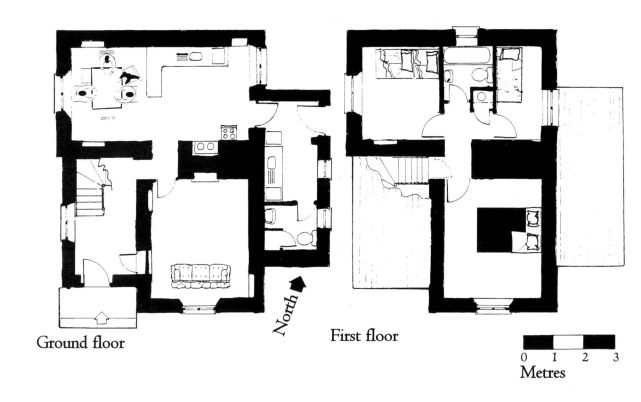

Ground floor

North

First floor

0   1   2   3
Metres

Gamekeeper's House has a high hall which leads to a comfortable sitting room with an open fire, TV & video. The long kitchen/dining room has modern fitted units. Cooking is by oil fired Rayburn stove and by gas hob, oven and microwave. There are also both dishwasher & washing machine. Beyond the utility room is a separate lavatory.

The first floor has one double bedroom, one single bedroom and a double bunk- room, and a bathroom with bath/shower, W.C. and basin. The house has oil-fired central heating. Full carpeting through the house, with terracotta tiles to the kitchen areas. Cots and high chairs can be provided. One or two well behaved dogs allowed.

Outside the woodland garden has lawns, and a terrace with garden furniture for sitting outside in the sunshine.

The house and garden are set on a rise with woodland on all sides and a little stream at the bottom. You reach Gamekeeper's by driving through Menabilly park and then turning down a half mile track through woodland. You can walk through the woods to the beach at Polridmouth which is about 600 metres away. Dogs Welcome.

Sleeps 5 & cot

Forgotten Houses Ltd
01326 340153 www.forgottenhouses.co.uk

The Gamekeeper's House

Menabilly, Fowey 64

Menabilly is a family estate and historic country house set in woodland on an unspoilt peninsular close to Fowey and St.Austell. The Gamekeeper's House was probably built around 1870, but modernised in the 1990s. Although part of a country house estate, it is far down a woodland track, and completely private, apart from the wildlife. It makes an ideal retreat, yet provides good access to the coastal footpath and to the beach at Polridmouth Cove 500 yards away.

The house was built with some style. It has thick walls, a steep slate roof, a great double chimney and charming architectural details. Apart from the old stone kennels down the slope it feels as though there is not another building in Cornwall. However, it is not far to the beach and two or three miles by car -or foot- to the lovely port of Fowey. This part of Cornwall has something to offer the visitor at all times of the year. There are festivals, sailing, and a beautiful little town at Fowey. The Eden Project is four miles away, and you can walk from the house along the coast - visit the tiny village & pub at Polkerris, or enjoy the small shops and bistros in Fowey and Lostwithiel. In spring, visit the gardens of Cornwall and see the profusion of Camellias, Rhododendrons, Daffodils and many other plants.

This is a lovely cottage in a unique position. It is not only a complete retreat, but also a well-placed base for visits elsewhere. Although there is a lot to tell of this house, it is enough to say that Gamekeeper's has been and remains a great favourite, much painted, written about, and remembered.

Forgotten Houses Ltd
01326 340153   www.forgottenhouses.co.uk

Littleworth

Bolventor, St Neot 70

Littleworth has two buildings.

The main house has two bedrooms downstairs, with a wide hall, and large bathroom with both bath & separate shower cubicle. A second WC room has the washing machine. Each bedroom also has a pull out bed. Upstairs, sitting room and kitchen form one large high beamed room with hardwood timber floors, rugs, 2 sofas, wood-burning stove, and fine painted wooden kitchen with long pine table, a butler sink, wooden dish-rack, catering style cooker, fridge, freezer & microwave. TV. Oil fired central heating. Door from the sitting room leads to south facing terrace with lawns and barbecue. Good views around the valley.

The Old Cottage (rather confusingly called "New House") is about twenty yards away. The cottage has a great stone chimney with open fire and flagstone floor. It has been renovated as one high ceilinged living room, stretching up to the roof. There is a small kitchen under the stairs. A smart shower room is under the open plan gallery, where there is a double bed, reached by a steep stair. Available separately out of season.

Private drive, & parking, large garden and fields. Trees. No Dogs in either building.

Friday Changeover Sleeps 4-8

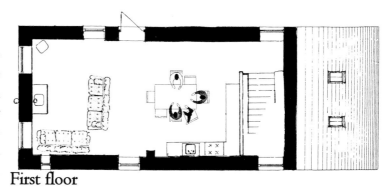

First floor

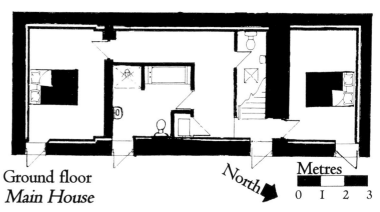

Ground floor
Main House

North   Metres
0 1 2 3

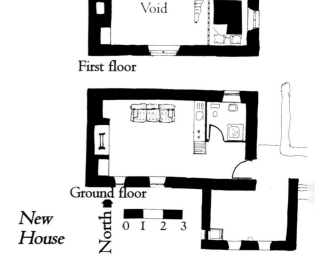

Void

First floor

Ground floor

New House

North
0 1 2 3

Littleworth

Some of the oldest houses in Cornwall are in the valleys running up from the sea to Bodmin Moor. At the top of the Fowey River valley in a south facing hollow, Littleworth was once two small farms and a couple of other buildings. There is a grove of trees around the house, from which are good views over the valley, and the almost invisible ruins of mediaeval villages.

This is an historic romantic place, surrounded by stones and the remnants of old buildings, with plenty to do and an easy walk to the lakes and moors above the valley. The lakes to the west of the house and the Fowey valley are beautiful places, but this is also a very good base for touring, with swift journeys possible all over the place. The renovation was finished in 2005. Once part of a great estate of farms, valleys, downland and moors, Littleworth and its historic surroundings are an interesting remnant of old style farming. It is a lovely spot of land once called the sweetest meadows of the district.

There are no close neighbours; you can enjoy a peaceful break and the landscape. The house is well placed behind Looe, Polperro, close to Bodmin, the romantic and wild Moors, and to the market town and castle of Launceston. The big sandy beaches of the north coast are about thirty minutes away.

New House, Littleworth

Forgotten Houses Ltd
01326 340153 www.forgottenhouses.co.uk

Dozmary,

Bolventor, St Neot 73

The house was renovated in 2006. Built against a bank, it has terraces to both sides. The owners have finished the house to a high standard and specification, including slate slab floors on the ground floor and the large first floor terrace. All upstairs floors are of oak boarding. The large combined sitting room and kitchen is well equipped. The sitting room has a wood burning stove and flat screen TV with DVD.

There are three bedrooms and the one downstairs has its own shower room. A second bathroom with shower over the bath is upstairs.

The kitchen has modern units with granite worktops; a square sink, washing machine, dishwasher, microwave, electric hob, double oven, fridge/freezer, and large pine table with benches. Oil fired central heating. The private drive slopes down to a large parking area with a stone outbuilding. There are walled lawns between house and lake, and a walled south terrace. The entrance side has lawns & granite steps to the first floor terrace. The lake is a few feet beyond the low garden wall. Good views over the lake and around the valley. Dogs allowed.

Sleeps 6

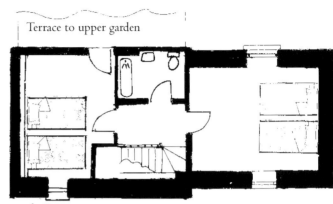

Terrace to upper garden

First floor

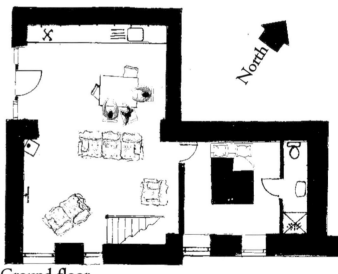

Ground floor

Metres

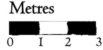

0   1   2   3

Dozmary,

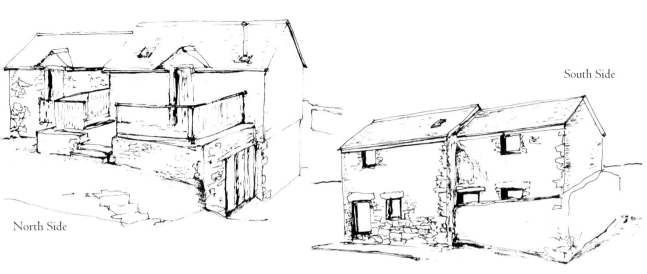

South Side

North Side

Few places can claim so unusual or romantic a setting. Dozmary is a lake in a high remote hollow where valleys from Bodmin Moor run south to the sea. Dozmary is not just of European archaeological importance, but also the subject of myth and legend. Stories tell that the water can rise and fall like the tide, that King Arthur's sword Excalibur was cast into the lake, that cattle cross it dry shod, that treasure lies beneath and that Giant Jan Tregeagle was sentenced to drain it with a sea shell. Once the site of annual festivals, the last "great revel" was in 1773. Dozmary is at the end of a long rebuilt track and although one other small cottage is close by, you are surrounded by fields and moor and feel miles from anywhere. In the 18th century, ice was cut and stored here for use in Fowey; you can still trace the granite ramps.

The house looks over the lake, the valley and five thousand years of history. The balconies, terraces and garden catch the sun and you can walk for miles around the house. You may fish in Dozmary. Colliford Lake, with many facilities, is close by. Since the main highway is only a couple of miles away, it is easy to reach the coast, to visit Lostwithiel, Bodmin, Launceston or to tour Cornwall - but most will want to stay, explore this enchanting rare place, and enjoy a fine and comfortable house.

Extract from: Richard Carew's Survey of Cornwall 1602

"In the midst of the wild moors of this hundred, far from any dwelling or river, there lieth a great standing water called Dosmery Pool, about a mile or better in compass, fed by no perceived spring, neither having any avoidance, until (of late) certain tinners brought an adit therefrom. The country people held many strange conceits of this pool, as, that it did ebb and flow, that it had a whirlpool in the midst thereof, and that a faggot once thrown thereinto was taken up at Foy haven, six miles distant. Wherefore, to try what truth rested in these reports, some gentleman dwelling not far off, caused a boat and nets to be carried thither overland. Fish they caught none, save a few eels upon hooks: the pool proved nowhere past a fathom and half deep, and for a great way very shallow. Touching the opinion of ebbing and flowing, it should seem to be grounded partly upon the increase which the rain floods brought thereinto from the bordering hills (which perhaps gave also the name, for doz is come, and maur great), and the decrease occasioned by the next drought, and partly for that the winds do drive the waves to and fro upon those sandy banks. And thus the miracle of Dosmery Pool deceased.
Of this wonder he said:
Dosmery Pool amidst the moors
On top stands of a hill;
More than a mile about no streams
It empt, nor any fill."

Forgotten Houses Ltd
01326 340153   www.forgottenhouses.co.uk

Harry's Court,

St Ives 77

Harry's Court is entered through an archway from the street, down steps into a small courtyard. The front door leads into the kitchen, newly designed and refitted (spring 2007). It has electric hob and cooker, microwave, washing machine, dishwasher, fridge/freezer. A breakfast table is by the window seats. Off the entrance area is a downstairs WC.

The large sitting room has a dining table at one end. At the other end are sofas round the fireplace (which has a gas fire). Fully carpeted with good furniture. This is a big room with large windows and window seat looking over the coast and above the beach. There is a second walk and sit-in bay window which looks over the beach and which also has a door to a long outside balcony.

In the corner is a winding stair to the first floor. The main bedroom with double bed has many modern fitted cupboards, a window seat to the wide window over the beach and a wash basin in the corner. The second bedroom is good sized and has a seated window bay over the sea and twin beds. The third smaller bedroom has twin beds and a wash basin in the corner.

Just before the main spacious well lit bathroom with bath, there is a separate walk in shower room. Electric heating.

About 20 metres away is a secure garage with one parking place. This is available at extra charge.   No Dogs.

Friday Changeover. Sleeps 6

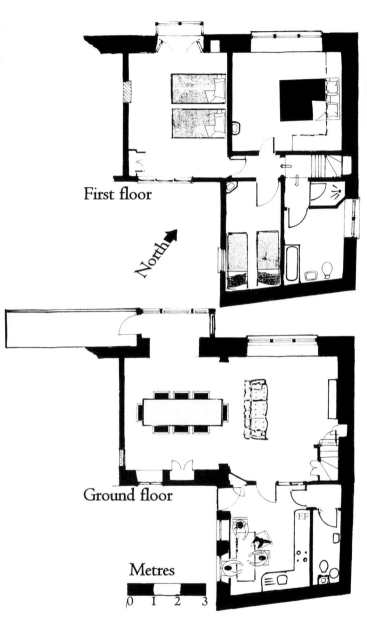

First floor

North

Ground floor

Metres

0   1   2   3

Forgotten Houses Ltd
01326 340153 www.forgottenhouses.co.uk

St Ives was once an important fishing and landing place. It is on the north coast about twenty miles from Lands End at the end of a curving bay often called one of the world's most beautiful. This has miles of sandy beaches. The town has a fifteenth century church and many small alleys and little streets lined by varied stone houses, all of which deserve exploration.

In 1801 a wall was built against the beach to improve protection for the fishermen. On this in turn were built cottages which, during the 19th century, had artists' studios on the first floor. Harry's Court is an intriguing, perhaps quaint, courtyard, once six small houses, now converted to three built along and behind that wall. 5, Harry's Court was two cottages. It has astonishing views from windows and balconies built over the beach. Here you can see the curving shore, the hills, the Island, the golden sands, the sea and surf. It really is an amazing place to visit and stay.

St Ives also has the Tate Modern and other galleries, and many small shops of quality, bistros, fish restaurants and smaller galleries, since St Ives has been a famous home of artists for 150 years. The coast south has magnificent cliffs and dramatic scenery. The town is charming and deservedly popular. The beach of fine sand is just one of many delights. The house provides a really good holiday, and is comfortable, accessible and in an astonishing position.

Forgotten Houses Ltd
01326 340153   www.forgottenhouses.co.uk

Forgotten Houses Ltd
01326 340153 www.forgottenhouses.co.uk

Forgotten Houses Ltd
01326 340153 www.forgottenhouses.co.uk

Higher Bosvarren

Little Pinnock Pella

Forgotten Houses Ltd
01326 340153 www.forgottenhouses.co.uk

The Long Little Pinnock

The Old House,
Little Pinnock

Forgotten Houses Ltd
01326 340153 www.forgottenhouses.co.uk

Higher Bosvarren Farmhouse

Constantine 9

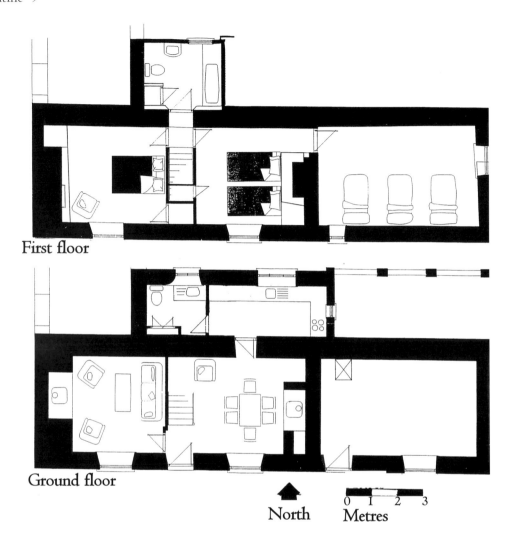

First floor

Ground floor

North   Metres

0 1 2 3

The house has been carefully renovated and simply decorated. The sitting room and dining room at Higher Bosvarren both have big granite fireplaces with wood burners, a stone bread oven. They are comfortable carpeted rooms. A long table seats 8. There is one bathroom and a second WC in the utility room downstairs which also includes a washing machine. The kitchen, refitted 2003, has electric cooker & hob, microwave; fridge-freezer.

There are three bedrooms, one of which is long and high ceilinged. Fitted carpets throughout, save terracotta tiles to kitchen and utility.

Oil fired <u>central heating</u>. Ping pong table on a cobbled floor in the stone barn adjoining the house. Private parking. Good south facing walled garden very safe for small children. Cot and high chair available. Bicycles possible on the farm tracks. Dogs allowed. A comfortable and interesting old house.

Sleeps 7 & Cot

Forgotten Houses Ltd
01326 340153   www.forgottenhouses.co.uk

Higher Bosvarren Farmhouse

Constantine 9

Bosvarren is about a mile from the Helford River, and close to the beaches and old sea port of Falmouth, Helston and the Lizard, the coasts, and many beaches in the area. The house is in a farm hamlet half a mile up a tree lined drive in wooded country of hills and streams. It's built of granite and represents the essential double ended farmhouses of the area, set at right angles to the hill, in trees and fields. Although the site, field names and features of the farm go back eight hundred years, the farm was rebuilt in the 16th and 17th centuries. The walls are two feet thick and there are two enormous fireplaces, one with bread oven. Both have wood burning stoves.

The bedrooms have strange angles and corners and one is large & high ceilinged. The house is pleasing, with a private barn, a cobbled terrace and an enclosed and private suntrap south-facing walled garden in front, with additional garden for children. It's in the middle of an estate round which you can walk, and particularly safe for children to play. There are riding stables near by.

The area around remains one of the most popular in Cornwall with good access to beaches, Falmouth, the Helford River and many visitor facilities. This is a popular house and suitable for many different types of holiday, and ages.

Forgotten Houses Ltd
01326 340153   www.forgottenhouses.co.uk

Little Pinnock Pella

Fowey 44

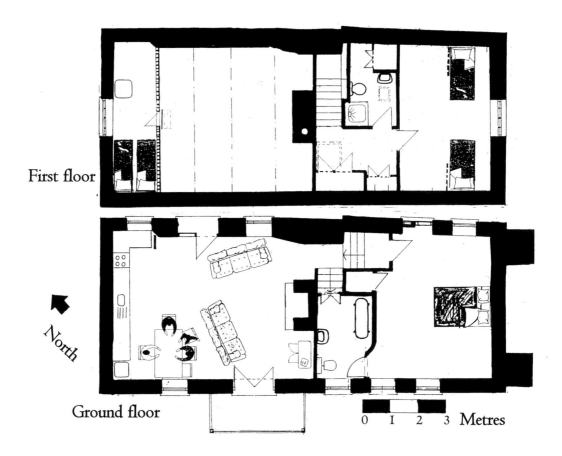

First floor

North

Ground floor

0 1 2 3 Metres

Little Pinnock Pella has been carefully renovated to high standards and with a simple careful interior design. The large high beamed sitting room has an open fireplace, slate hearth and two sofas, television, DVD & video. Up one end is a fine fitted kitchen with electric cooker & oven, big fridge/freezer, microwave, dishwasher and washer/drier.

There is a large square oak table in a light and delightful interior. Above the kitchen area is an open gallery, reached by an amazing sliding ladder, where there are two narrow mattresses under the eaves. The gallery has a spring loaded gate.

One of the two bedrooms is a double room with bathroom, with Victorian roll top bath. The other has two twin beds and its own top lit shower room. Bedrooms are carpeted and the sitting room has boards with loose rugs. Radio and CD player. Boardgames and puzzles

Oil fired central heating. Large terrace looking over south facing garden; good and private parking. Dogs allowed. Can be rented with The Old House, Little Pinnock, to sleep up to 12

Sleeps 4-6

Forgotten Houses Ltd
01326 340153   www.forgottenhouses.co.uk

Little Pinnock Pella

LITTLE PINNOCK
MARCH 2002
SCDI.

Fowey with its peninsula is one of the glories of Cornwall. Close by is the tiny estuary village of Golant, with church, pub & restaurant. Castle Dore, the iron age fort, is just up the hill to the north. The house is not far from the fishing village of Polkerris and is close to the Eden Project, Fowey, Lostwithiel and Restormel Castle, Bodmin Moor and to beaches and a whole host of activities including a golf course, Trenython Manor Country Club and places to visit, both coast and country.

The nearest country pub is at Golant, about a mile away. Just north of Fowey, Little Pinnock was a mediaeval farming hamlet, in a sheltered south facing valley. There was once a great mansion here, but for a couple of hundred years just two stone built farmsteads. These are of such great interest that a considerable archaeological investigation was recently made of the site. Early last century a farmhouse was built some 200 yards away from the old hamlet and the old farmhouse and buildings abandoned until recently renovated. Little Pinnock Pella, which is down a long drive in pretty and private country, looks over the pasture and valley to the west.

The renovation of the building was well thought out. The stone walls are thick even by Cornish standards; the high roof of the main living area, with its fireplace and gallery, provides an atmospheric and spacious house. The house is comfortable, has modern equipment, central heating. Outside are old tracks, eleven acres and garden down to a little stream.

The Long Little Pinnock

Fowey 65

The Long Little Pinnock was renovated in summer 2004, and has, as its name suggests, a very long living room with fine planked floor, wood burning stove and kitchen, underneath a gallery at the far end, with the two storey section beyond that. The gable end of the living room is all glass & looks south west over the valley. The building is of stone under a slate roof with exposed high trusses and roof beams.

As well as two main bedrooms, one with bathroom, one with shower room, there is also a quaint small bedroom with one single bed. The gallery, reached off a curving circular timber stair, has two extra beds. Modern newly fitted kitchen with every appliance including dishwasher. The sitting room has leather sofas, carefully chosen furniture, TV & DVD, radio and CD player. Board games and puzzles. Washing machine and tumble dryer. Oil fired under floor central heating.

Private garden running down to the stream includes remnants of another mediaeval house, mature trees and is naturally sheltered. A second higher private garden is reached across a bridge from the first floor. Private parking behind stone walls off a 400 yard track from the road. Dogs allowed. Can be taken with one other house at Little Pinnock for larger groups.

Sleeps 5-7

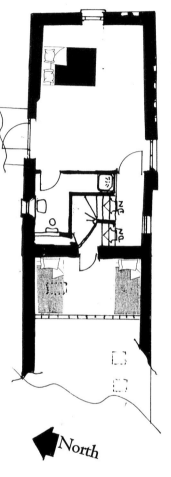

North

Metres

0 1 2 3

First floor

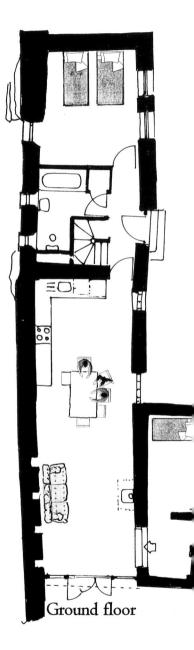

Ground floor

The Long Little Pinnock

Fowey 65

The Long Little Pinnock, on the south coast of Cornwall, once formed the outbuilding to one of the two mediaeval farms at Little Pinnock, a mile or so north of Fowey, within a sheltered valley.

The building has been rebuilt and extended a number of times and for different uses- perhaps even quarry work, since its first big rebuild in the 17th century. A small part may once have been a dwelling attached to a barn . Inside there are candle niches and chicken squares in the wall, pigeon holes in the side and gable, and a quirky layout, including high beamed roof, circular staircase, gallery, and bridge to the upper garden. The house is built of old stone with some from a much older building, and looks south across the valley with particularly good views from the first floor.

Newly renovated to a high standard, this is a fine holiday base not only because there are so many places to visit and see close by, but also because you and your family can stay happily in the house. There is a good sized garden, which includes the ruins of another old house. Beaches are only a mile or two away, Golant has a good pub, and Fowey is charming with bistros, small shops, pubs and harbour. The house sleeps up to 7 but can provide for larger parties if combined with one of the other houses at Little Pinnock. The renovation, fitting out & decor scheme have been well done and help to ensure that this is an interesting holiday house of high standard in a good position.

Forgotten Houses Ltd
01326 340153 www.forgottenhouses.co.uk

The Old House

Little Pinnock Fowey 63

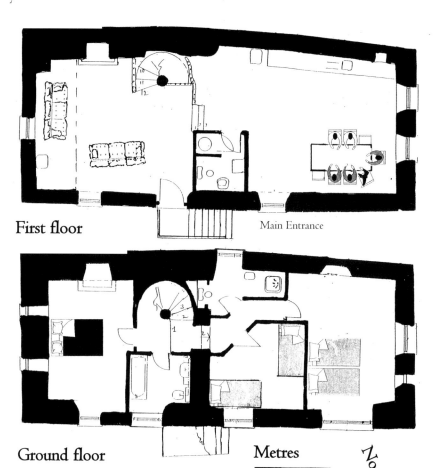

First floor

Main Entrance

An open gallery over
the sitting room has
two low beds

Ground floor

Metres

0 1 2 3

North

Renovation of The Old House was finished in 2004. The entrance is up stone steps and the large sitting room has new furniture, window seats & wood burner. Television & DVD. 3 steps up lead to a large well lit kitchen with maple units & teak worktop, stainless steel sink & dishwasher, big fridge/freezer with ice dispenser. Double catering style oven with electric ceramic hobs. Microwave. Good sized oak table with extra chairs to seat 8. Utility room has lavatory, Siemens washing machine & drier.

Both ground & first floor have planked floors. Oil fired central heating - underfloor to ground floor. Fine circular wood stair down to 3 bedrooms, bathroom with Victorian bath. Large walk in shower room includes mediaeval door. Both bathrooms are tiled. The main bedroom has second 16th century fireplace and ornate heavily carved bed. Other double bedroom has a second TV, & door opening onto the garden and plenty of windows with wide window shelves. Twin bedroom has big pine beds. Spacious, well fitted and equipped. Gardens & private parking. Garden furniture. Can be taken with neighbouring houses at Little Pinnock Pella or Long Little Pinnock. Dogs allowed. **Sleeps 6**

Forgotten Houses Ltd
01326 340153   www.forgottenhouses.co.uk

The Old House

Little Pinnock Fowey 63

The Old House is part of a restored mediaeval farming hamlet. This is a seriously old, interesting house. Its position in the landscape emphasizes that this has always been a most desirable place for a house in south Cornwall. The archaeologists had two sessions here, finding 12th century pottery at one end. The walls are up to 5 feet thick and include pieces obtained from Tywardreath Priory, demolished after 1538.

There are some 35 pieces of carved church stone- how many can you find? The walls are of creamy brown slatey stone under an irregularly coursed slate roof with a small catslide roof of tiny slates over the front door. Two old fireplaces include one whose hearth stone is perhaps from the Priory Kitchen. Outside is a massive stone chimney. The circular stair is built around a post which reaches high into the ceiling.

There are many interesting features such as the pigeon holes cut in the walls, the door frame of 1450, narrow windows or low windows, the high beamed roof, the fine joinery work, old fireplaces or the two wall lights made from two Victorian ridge tiles. The Old House is some 4ft wider than most other Cornish buildings of its style and age. Not only does this provide unusual space and width but it suggests that it must have been a house of some importance.

This is a wonderful, interesting and well restored house. It is not far to beaches, or to the little port of Fowey with its bistros, shops and pubs. The house is in a charming south facing valley, and is a fine touring base for visiting other parts of Cornwall.

Forgotten Houses Ltd
01326 340153 www.forgottenhouses.co.uk

Wreckers, Trevoyan

Tower House, Boconnoc

Forgotten Houses Ltd
01326 340153 www.forgottenhouses.co.uk

The Groom's House

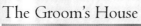

Head Grooms

Forgotten Houses Ltd
01326 340153 www.forgottenhouses.co.uk

Wreckers, Trevoyan

St Merryn   50

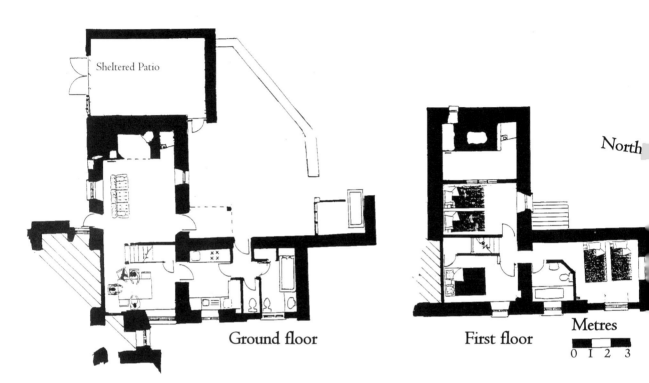

Sheltered Patio

Ground floor

First floor

North

Metres

0 1 2 3

Wreckers has its own entrance down a narrow high walled track from the road, past the back of Trevoyan. Parking is outside the courtyard and garden which faces west & towards the sea. Here also is the old well house with a large granite trough. In the cobbled courtyard are doors to the sitting room and into the kitchen lobby. Off this lobby is also a bathroom and separate second WC. The kitchen has fridge freezer, washing machine and slate tiled floor. From the kitchen is a door to the dining room with rugs over large slate slabs, which is also the floor for the sitting room with TV, DVD, open fireplace, and ceiling showing the trusses high in the roof. From the sitting room is also a door to the small lawn to the south.

The garden is on two sides and there is a pond in the farmyard. The walls have some stones showing, together with many old timbers. Upstairs are three bedrooms all fully and newly carpeted and a second bathroom. Gas fired central heating. Dogs allowed. Not the most suitable garden for toddlers. Wreckers is separate and private from Trevoyan, but can be combined with Trevoyan by opening of two sound-insulated doors.

The garden was extended in 2005, & a paddock is available for games. A charming and unusual house with many quaint features, well fitted out, and popular with visitors. **Sleeps 6**

Forgotten Houses Ltd
01326 340153   www.forgottenhouses.co.uk

Wreckers, Trevoyan

St Merryn   50

The north coast between Newquay and Padstow has some of the best known beaches for both swimming and surfing and is also a good base for exploring the rest of Cornwall. This old house at Trevoyan is listed as exceptional because of age, character and features and was built in a sheltered plateau just inland from the sea, on the coast road between Porthcothnan and St Merryn, with easy access to Constantine Bay and the seven beaches of the Parish.

In later centuries a bigger house was built on the front, which has taken the name Trevoyan. It was only in 2003 that the older part of the house, which rises from great boulders in the ground, was renovated to make a separate holiday wing with its own garden, entrance and courtyard. This wing is built of layered thick slate stone, with some earth filled walls, some part slate hung. It is roughly 'L' shaped under a rag slate roof. There is one of the deepest fireplaces we have seen, with separate fireplace, bread oven, smoke chamber and a small platform (with its own window) where children used to sleep. Now there is a high hall, dining room and three bedrooms and two bathrooms. Like Trevoyan to which it is attached at one corner, this is a charming house in a great position.

There are fields on all sides and views to the horizon to the sea. Beyond the garden behind the house are a large listed barn, further barns, an ornamental garden with pond & ducks. In addition to the courtyard there is an area of private garden. The layout and furnishing is comfortable rather than modern, with many old features retained. This is a fine old listed house in the countryside, great for the seaside and also for touring. (See also the entries for Trevoyan and Swallows).

Forgotten Houses Ltd
01326 340153   www.forgottenhouses.co.uk

Waggon House,

Pennant, Port Isaac   74

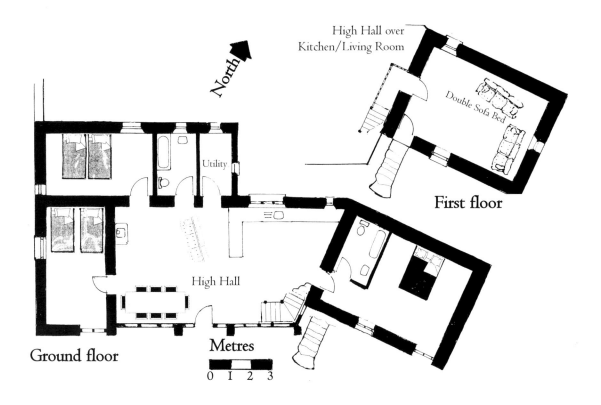

High Hall over
Kitchen/Living Room

Double Sofa Bed

First floor

Utility

High Hall

Ground floor

Metres

0 1 2 3

The Waggon House was renovated during 2007 by experienced designers and is large and spacious. The layout is based around the large main kitchen/family room, which has a long wall of windows recessed behind the granite pillars outside. The ceiling stretches right up past timber beams to the corners of the roof. This room has a wood burning stove in the corner, a table in the window and a new kitchen with electric oven and hob, microwave, dishwasher, fridge and washer/drier.

Off the kitchen are the utility room, a dowstairs bathroom with shower over bath, two bedrooms each with twin beds and views over fields. The third, master bedroom has its own bathroom.

The open plan stairs wind up the side of the main room to the first floor sitting room which has TV, DVD and CD player. One sofa can be converted to a double bed. Wood floor to first floor, plain light green carpets downstairs. Oil fired central heating. An irregular set of old stone steps goes outside up to the sitting room.

Outside there is plenty of private parking off the old farmyard. The garden is not large, but has a brick built barbecue, and there is plenty of space around the house and on the farm for children to play, wander or bike. Garden furniture. There is a small pond about thirty yards from the house. Most of the house is on a single floor and therefore suitable for those less able to climb stairs. Dogs allowed.

**Could be taken with Josiah's to sleep 12.
Sleeps 6 to 8**

Forgotten Houses Ltd
01326 340153   www.forgottenhouses.co.uk

Waggon House

The Waggon House is at Pennant Farm. You turn off the lane just after Endellion Church to go down a drive. From this, you look along the dramatic coast of North Cornwall, and over the lovely village of Port Isaac. This is one of the most popular holiday areas of Cornwall, and the views help explain why this is and why it is so often used for films and TV shows. Close by are cliffs, walks, small beaches or larger sandy beaches such as Polzeath. There are pubs, restaurants and lots to do. However at Pennant farm, you are surrounded by fields and have the best of all worlds.

Pennant is a traditional mixed farm and still occupied by the family that has lived there for generations. The modern farm buildings are some way from and separate from the old stone buildings.

The Waggon House was built alongside a fine two storey barn built for grain above and stock below. This double hipped building is of exceptional quality, has fine ashlar granite blocks to the south with good quoins, brick soldier arches and was probably built towards the end of the eighteenth century. Alongside this was built, as its name suggests, a large long open shed for carts and large wagons which was then extended further to the rear. Beyond this, was a stone barn for horses. The whole makes a large, good looking and interesting house, and the surroundings live up to it. The site is ancient, but in the 18th century the buildings were spread round the farmyard. This is itself charming- and ensures privacy. This is a comfortable house in a popular part of Cornwall.

The Tower House,

Boconnoc, Lostwithiel 72

Entrance to the Tower House is from the north, to the right of the main front and up a path to the first floor.

A small hall has cupboard, stairs, WC and door to the family room with views over the church, and a small kitchen. This has electric cooker and hob, microwave, fridge. TV and video in this room.

The hall leads through another larger lobby to the "King Charles Bedroom", an enormous room with big windows looking over the park and church. This is fitted as a sitting room, with fine working fireplace, high ceilings. It has two single beds.

Upstairs there are two bedrooms with good quality furniture, one with double bed and one with twin beds. One looks west and one east. Between them is a newly refitted bathroom with panelling and charm.

The north or tower wing has oil fired central heating. The laundry room is up steps in a separate building. After a long drive through the park, there is plenty of parking either by the house or in the yard to the North. Renovated and refitted 2004 to 2007 to high standard. Sports available include fishing. Lots of garden. Extra dramatic and interesting rooms are planned as additions during 2007.
No Dogs.

Friday Changeover Sleeps 6
or perhaps more.

A room modelled on the great state rooms of the liner *Queen Mary*, together with a further large bedroom and bathroom to the second floor are planned for completion in 2007.

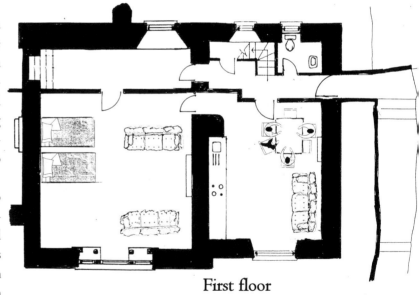

Metres

0 1 2 3

North

Second floor

First floor

The Tower House,

Boconnoc was a mediaeval power centre, and the much disguised mediaeval hall is still at the heart of the house. Although the roof trusses are from 1579, the house was renovated by the Pitt Family, and so has been a family house for three of Britain's prime ministers. It has fine Georgian features although with Victorian alterations. Since it has now lost a wing or two, Boconnoc is rather smaller than it used to be. The house and estate remain a family affair, and the house has been in that family's ownership since purchased in 1720.

This great house has a mile and a half of drive, an eighteenth century landscaped park, a large lake, Tudor deer park, little valleys, monuments, church and hidden up the hill the yards and buildings that were needed in its heyday. After being unoccupied for many years, and nationally listed as an endangered building, the house has now been restored. The North wing includes a Victorian Tower of 1862, now reduced in height, which was designed to allow direct access from the first floor to the mediaeval church close by.

This entrance from the hill is now the entrance to the North wing and Tower house. This includes the large room, with venetian windows known as the King Charles bedroom since Charles I held court here during one of his periods of success.

The tower is quirky, but newly fitted out, and the views from the windows to the church, and to the park are astonishing. The gardens are well maintained, and there is lots to see and do on the estate, but it is also a good touring base from which to explore Cornwall. The nearest cliff beaches are about fifteen minutes away and the beaches of the north coast rather further. The ancient towns of Lostwithiel and Fowey are not far. It is difficult to sum up this great house and landscape, save to say that arriving here always raises your spirits and makes you content, no matter what has been happening elsewhere.

Forgotten Houses Ltd
01326 340153 www.forgottenhouses.co.uk

The Grooms House

Boconnoc, Lostwithiel 7

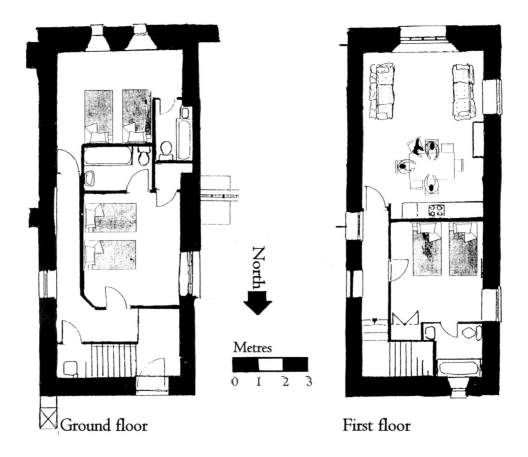

Ground floor　　　　　**First floor**

The Grooms House is on two floors and the renovation won a rare conservation design award. The stone buildings, built around 1770, are on the south east side of the stable yard, right by the church. The house is in one of the most beautiful locations in Cornwall. In the main building are three bedrooms and three bathrooms, a hall, modern fitted kitchen including dishwasher, microwave The sitting room has a stunning high ceiling and lantern light. TV & DVD. Stairway and first floor are panelled. Smart interior and fittings.

The first floor has polished boards and scatter rugs. There is a slate floor in the hall & full carpeting downstairs. Oil fired central heating. Washing machine in outside utility. There is plenty of secure parking, and safe recreation and playing areas in the enormous grounds. Dogs allowed by arrangement. Brown trout fishing at £17.00 per day. Bring own rods although some old rods available. No dogs.

Friday Changeover Sleeps 6
Can combine with Head Grooms to sleep 12-14

Forgotten Houses Ltd
01326 340153 www.forgottenhouses.co.uk

The Grooms House

Boconnoc, Lostwithiel   7

Boconnoc is one of the great houses of the west, with long drives through the parkland to its own mediaeval church, the house and an historic estate hamlet in a beautiful stretch of country. Once the power base of Cornwall, the estate remains the family concern it's been since 1720.

The buildings serving the house include a late c18th listed stable yard which looks over the little church, and Boconnoc mansion. One corner of the stable yard included quarters for the grooms, now restored to offer comfort and additional space. It is built of thick stone walls and has boarded rooms, high ceilings and many quirky features including skylight, curved stonework, two slot windows and window seats. The fine sitting room looks through a high arched window to views over the church and parkland.

Little known and seldom visited, it is a pleasure to come in through the private park laid out in the eighteenth century, past monuments, walks, drives, distant views, game birds and the deer in the deer park.

You may not want to leave Boconnoc, but it is close to Lostwithiel, Restormel Castle, the Eden Project, Liskeard, Bodmin Moor. The sea to the south is some 15 minutes away. A marvellous centre for summer activities, or for a winter break. Grooms has proved a much loved house and is one of those houses to which visitors return again and again.

Forgotten Houses Ltd
01326 340153 www.forgottenhouses.co.uk

Head Grooms

Boconnoc, Lostwithiel 79

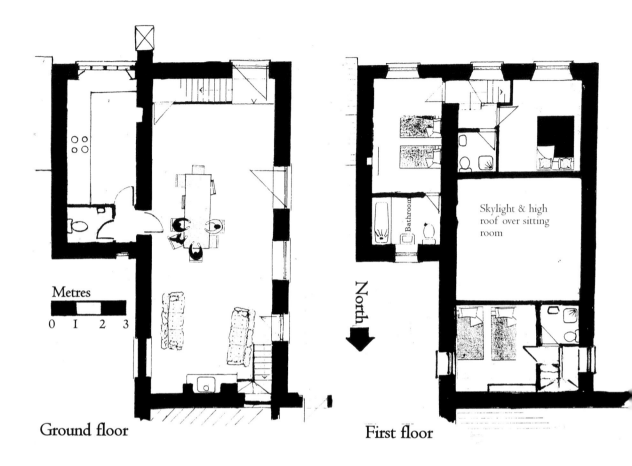

Ground floor

North

Skylight & high
roof over sitting
room

Bathroom

Metres

0 1 2 3

First floor

Head Grooms has been refitted (2004 to 2007) to a high standard, and retains many features from a varied history. The sitting room takes up much of the ground floor and has no first floor above it. Not only is it some 11.5 metres (40ft) long but it has a high skylight. There is a lower ceilinged fireplace area at one end, large woodburner, sofas, and a large dining table at the other. Loose carpets over part slate floors. Off this room is a downstairs lavatory and, beyond this, a newly fitted kitchen.

The kitchen has electric cooker and hob, fridge-freezer, microwave, a good level of equipment and a small table. The washing machine is in a laundry room in a separate building a few paces away. From the main room, a panelled stair-case leads up to two newly decorated and fitted bedrooms, both fully carpeted, one with a bathroom and the other a shower room.

At the other end of the main room a new narrow stair leads up to a well lit third bedroom and shower room (due for completion winter 2007). Oil fired central heating. After the long drive through the park, there is plenty of parking. Sports available include fishing. Lots of garden. Two extra put-up beds available.

Dogs allowed only by arrangement.
Friday Changeover   Sleeps 6-8
Can combine with Grooms to sleep 12-14

Head Grooms

Boconnoc remains one of the great estates of the south west. The stable yard, probably designed by Thomas Pitt III around 1770, and perhaps altered by John Soane in 1787, remains a rare eighteenth century example of the great yard. There were alterations in the nineteenth century which extended this quirky large house at one corner of the yard. There is no first floor over the sitting room which stretches right up to the roof light. The house is spacious, and because Boconnoc is so magical a place, you may not wish to go out. The estate has many miles of private road, an 18th century landscape park, lake, deer park, mediaeval church, great house, gardens. It is also possible to take part in country sports such as fishing.   The estate also holds events such as the Royal Cornwall Flower Show, a steam fair, dog show and other events. These do not affect the privacy of your stay but can provide a great day out, only a walk away.

From Boconnoc, it is only a few minutes to Lostwithiel an antiques centre and fascinating mediaeval town, to Lerryn, a picturesque river port, to Lanhydrock or to many other places. The Eden Project is about fifteen minutes away and the nearest good beach is a small cove about 15 minutes south.

Head Grooms is an unusual house newly refitted, and comfortable. The location is marvellous and makes for an exceptional holiday.

Forgotten Houses Ltd
01326 340153 www.forgottenhouses.co.uk

Treveddoe
Farmhouse

Bosbenna

Forgotten Houses Ltd
01326 340153   www.forgottenhouses.co.uk

Lower Bosvarren Farmhouse

Bosvarren House

Forgotten Houses Ltd
01326 340153 www.forgottenhouses.co.uk

Treveddoe Farmhouse

Warleggan Bodmin 53

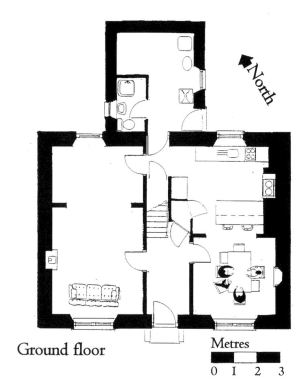

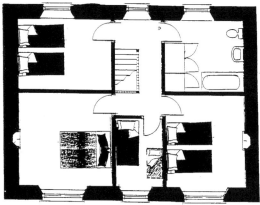

Ground floor

Metres

0 1 2 3

First floor

Treveddoe, redecorated and overhauled in 2006, has a large sitting room which is spacious, light & comfortable with woodburning stove, TV & video, DVD & CD player. The big kitchen/dining room runs from the front to the back & is kept snug by an oil-fired Rayburn. It is well equipped including dishwasher, electric cooker, microwave, fridge/freezer. At the back, the utility & laundry room with washing machine & drier has a boiler & a cloakroom with a <u>shower</u> and WC. A stable door leads to the enclosed back yard. Upstairs there are 3 double and one single bedrooms, and a generous sized bathroom.

Clothes dry well on the old-fashioned hoist above the Rayburn. There is a small paved, partially walled garden in the front, giving onto a large mown area bounded on all sides by a Cornish bank. Natural spring water supply. Shared use with Barley Crush of ping pong table in big barn, which is available for activities on a wet day. Central heating, electricity and logs are included in the rent. Private parking. The Barley Crush is some 40 yards away and the two can be rented together to take up to 12. Payphone. Staxrgates to stairs. Dogs allowed.

Friday Changeover   Sleeps 7 & cot

Forgotten Houses Ltd
01326 340153   www.forgottenhouses.co.uk

Treveddoe Farmhouse

Warleggan Bodmin 53

Treveddoe is a stone farmhouse built on the site of an Elizabethan Manor. It looks south with uninterrupted views over its own farmland, on which sheep and South Devon cattle graze. The fields behind the house at the top of the farm lead onto Bodmin Moor. The moorland river Warleggan marks the southern boundary. There is a large garden and good walks through the 25 acres of ancient woodland. The bluebells, wood anemones and foxgloves are beautiful in the spring and early summer. Historic Treveddoe Mine (tin and copper), now almost hidden by nature, is nearby, with evidence of the old workings in the river valley.

The farm is a bird-watcher's paradise and ideal for those who want a break away from the bustle and noise of everyday life. It is a tranquil and unique base from which to enjoy the best of Cornwall. Both north and south coasts are within easy reach, as are many Cornish gardens.

Treveddoe has provided great holidays for all ages. Children find the farm itself is exciting and intriguing, and the sea is not far away. The tranquility appeals to the parents, and the house is well laid out and easy to run. There is plenty of space downstairs.

There are many places to visit not far away but sometimes of course it is lovely to do nothing but enjoy the spectacular views.

Forgotten Houses Ltd
01326 340153 www.forgottenhouses.co.uk

Bosbenna

Constantine 36

Bosbenna is one of the most spacious and interesting of houses. There is a large sitting room, two sofas, TV & large open granite fireplace and wood burning stove. The large high kitchen and breakfast room has a long table, long worktops, built in electric oven and inset hob, a microwave, fridge/freezer, washing machine. There are three bedrooms plus two beds in a carpeted attic reached by ladder for children or agile adults.

One bathroom has freestanding Victorian bath, the other has WC & shower. Boiler room/drying room. Floors are stained or white limed boards with kelims & scatter rugs, terracotta tiles to bathrooms, changes of level, fitted carpets in bedrooms; many interesting features, including plank doors, high roofs, thick walls, granite dividers in a bedroom, and lots of books to read.

A part cobbled and part lawn enclosed courtyard to one side, a long lawn to the south and an enclosed garden to the east and north. Child's slide. Cot & high chair available. Good private parking. Safe for children. Oil fired central heating.

Access to surrounding farmland. Good for dogs.

Sleeps 8 & Cot

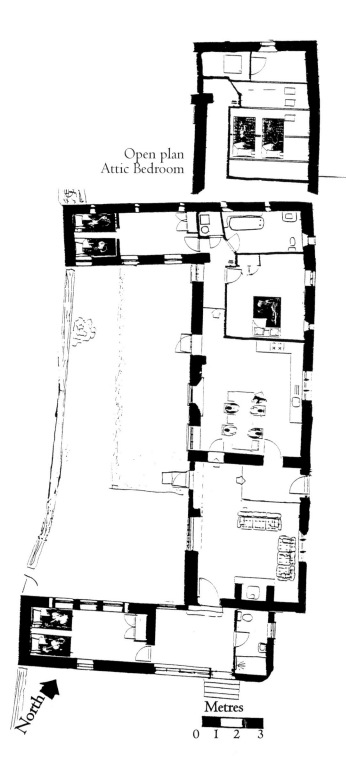

Open plan
Attic Bedroom

North

Metres
0 1 2 3

Forgotten Houses Ltd
01326 340153 www.forgottenhouses.co.uk

Bosbenna

Constantine 36

Bosbenna is in the hamlet of Bosvarren, about three miles from the beaches of Falmouth. Riding stables are half a mile away. Bosbenna is up a pretty farm drive, with plenty of room for children, dogs and walks on the surrounding wooded arable farm. Bosbenna is built round three sides of a cobbled and grassed suntrap courtyard & is a show case renovation. It is a large, thick walled house with high ceilings that show the old timber frames and has lots of space. The many windows, of different sizes and shapes from timber mullioned to stone slot, give the house a very light interior. The building has a big-stoned chimney and wonderful scantle slate roof - perhaps 17,000 slates - with big overhangs and no modern gutters. The 8 ft front door is up gran-ite slab steps, into a stone floored lobby. There are changes of level around the building. The bedrooms are well separated and of decent size (one has vertical granite slabs at the bed foot). The attic - very popular with children - is reached by a ladder and is the ideal secret place with two beds. The south lobby/sunroom has an old fashioned rocking horse and steps to the south lawn and meadow beyond. The cobbled courtyard to the west has plenty of sheltered space to enjoy the sun. Bosvarren Farmhouse, with its walled yard and garden, is some forty yards to the west; fields are to south and west.

This is a roomy and comfortable 'flagship' house in a good position. The house has given great pleasure to its visitors.

Forgotten Houses Ltd
01326 340153 www.forgottenhouses.co.uk

Lower Bosvarren Farmhouse

Constantine, Falmouth 11

Lower Bosvarren has two comfortable sitting rooms, each with sofas, enormous granite fireplaces and wood burning stoves. TV. The long breakfast room and kitchen have some exposed granite walls and a big table. The outer kitchen is beyond it.

There are four good sized double bedrooms. One bedroom has king size bed & duvet. There are two bathrooms. The one upstairs has a shower over the bath, and downstairs there is a large walk in shower. The kitchen has a built in oven, inset hob, microwave, fridge. The outer kitchen has dishwasher, washing machine, fridge freezer and oil fired boiler.

All rooms have fitted carpets save for tiles in the utility and vinyl in the kitchen and bathroom. The house was redecorated in 2004 & 6. The rooms are all of unusual proportions and shapes & include areas of granite stonework and two granite bread ovens.

Good for children. Cot and high chair available. Large south facing lawns and yard and range of renovated old stone barns. Private parking and enclosed yard and garden. Oil fired central heating. Walks around farmland. Dogs allowed.

Sleeps 8 & Cot

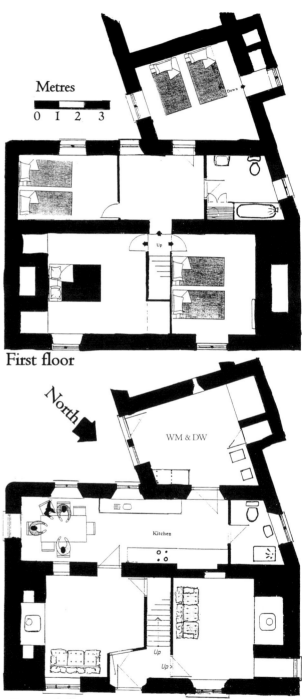

Metres
0 1 2 3

First floor

North

WM & DW

Kitchen

Up

Up

Ground floor

Lower Bosvarren Farmhouse

Constantine, Falmouth II

Lower Bosvarren, a listed Elizabethan farmhouse, is in the little farming hamlet of Bosvarren, up a tree-lined drive in unspoilt country four miles west of Falmouth. It retains its arched stone front door and much remains of the original 1620s renovation. Extended in the late eighteenth century and the early nineteenth century, there is a fair amount of space.

This was the most important farm in the hamlet, once one of the richer in the parish. It's a Celtic site built well down the hill, and with granite built two storey barns behind the house. The garden and courtyard are a natural sun trap and very good for children, barbecues and sunbathing. Bosbenna is about 40 yards away behind walls, across the track.

The house has been renovated so as to retain its original appearance and features, including its slate roof of small scantles. The outer kitchen includes yet a third enormous fireplace which may have been for feeding pressganged sailors, or if you are more prosaic, nineteenth century pigs.

The surrounding countryside, part of an estate, is open for walks, or exploration. There are beaches of differing types close at hand and Falmouth, Helston, the Lizard Peninsula and south west Cornwall are all within half an hour's drive. There is a prize winning pub a couple of miles away. Small children can bike round the tracks of the farm; horse riding stables close by. This is a popular and happy house.

Forgotten Houses Ltd
01326 340153 www.forgottenhouses.co.uk

Bosvarren House

Falmouth 35

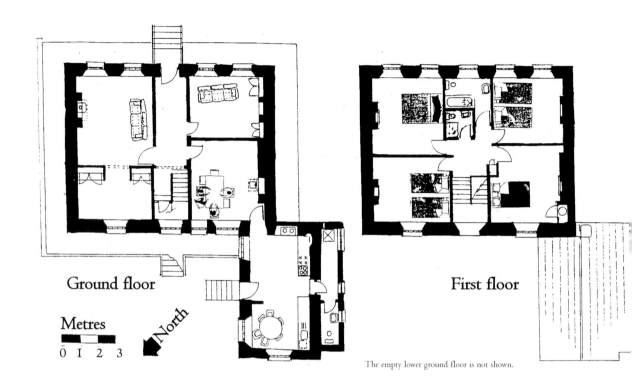

Ground floor

Metres

0 1 2 3

North

First floor

The empty lower ground floor is not shown.

Bosvarren House is on three floors, although the garden basement is unused. The garden runs round all four sides. The south front looks over the garden and has wide granite steps and a fine granite ashlar front. Entry is usually from a small rear courtyard to the kitchen wing. The <u>large</u> kitchen has breakfast area, dishwasher, oil fired cooking range, electric cooker, ceramic hob, microwave, fridge/freezer. Next to the kitchen is a small utility with washing machine, drier and separate WC. The house has shutters & window seats to all the sash windows. The central hall has the original front door and fanlight, and there are many other fine features including mahogany doors and original fireplaces. There is a dining room, a sitting room with fine cupboards, a large sitting room with TV & fireplace and the original Turkish style arch to a small study area. Most floors are covered with fitted carpets. Both sitting and dining rooms have wood burning stoves. Upstairs are four good looking double bedrooms, two with double beds, two with twin beds. There is one full bathroom, & a second shower room with basin & WC. Redecorated 2006. Lots of books to read around the house. Secondary electric heating. Cot and high chair available. Plenty of parking space. Dogs allowed.

Friday Changeover Sleeps 8 & Cot

Forgotten Houses Ltd
01326 340153 www.forgottenhouses.co.uk

Bosvarren House

Bosvarren House is in open country between Constantine and Falmouth. This is the big house of a small farming hamlet of two farms and a couple of cottages and is approached up a private drive. Nearby is the Helford River and the Lizard with dramatic scenery and beaches. The sea is a couple of miles away but it is three miles to the three beaches at Falmouth and only half an hour to surfing beaches on the north coast. Falmouth is charming, and the new Maritime Museum, like the Eden Project, is worth a visit.

The little hamlet of Bosvarren is up a tree lined drive from the country road, and Bosvarren House has two drives opening off that track. Around the house are nearly two acres of garden, including a lot of lawn, some good trees, and a number of raised beds and many shrubs. This Georgian house was built around 1812 to impress. It has a south front of granite ashlar and became the country residence of the rector of Constantine. There are great views around the countryside. There is a riding stable near by, across the road.

The surrounding farm land is in the same ownership as the house, so it is possible to walk freely and widely. Bosvarren House stands in the middle of gardens full of flowering shrubs, with small and large areas of lawns. Raised beds and mature trees make the garden varied and interesting. Though not as smart as some, Bosvarren House is comfortable, spacious, stylish and with a lovely garden which is particularly liked by children.

Pencobben

Trevoyan

Forgotten Houses Ltd
01326 340153 www.forgottenhouses.co.uk

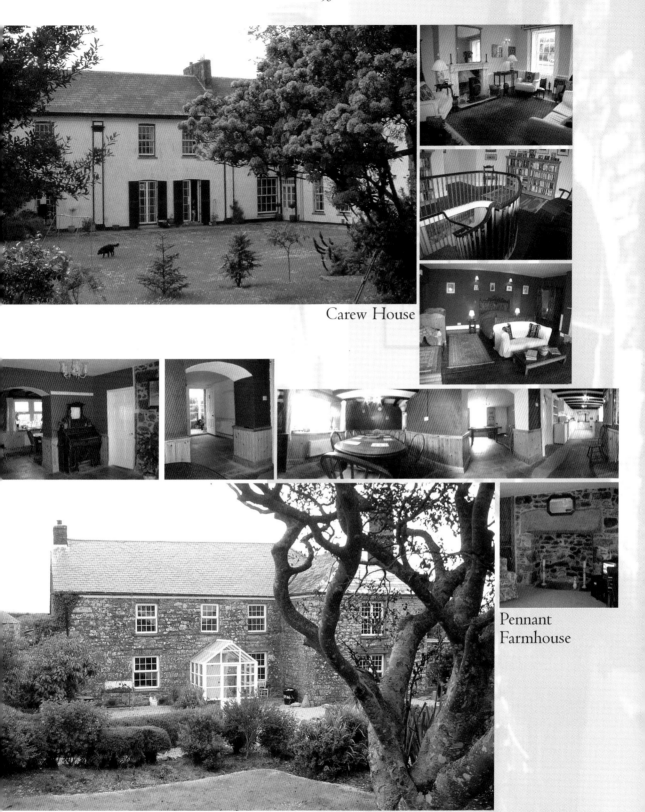

Carew House

Pennant
Farmhouse

Forgotten Houses Ltd
01326 340153 www.forgottenhouses.co.uk

Pencobben

Godrevy Point St Ives Bay 31

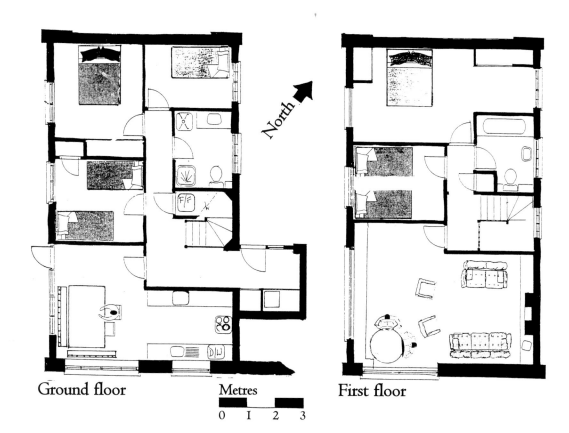

Ground floor

Metres

0 1 2 3

First floor

North

Pencobben's sitting room on the first floor has views over the countryside and has table, 3 sofas, 2 armchairs, fireplace, TV and lots of books. The Kitchen downstairs also has a big table with chairs & benches, electric cooker & oven, small fridge, dishwasher. Coffee maker. Microwave. A big fridge freezer is under the stairs.

The house has five bedrooms, which can sleep 9 people, including two double beds. Two bathrooms (one with shower). A big washing machine and separate drier.

The house was plainly redecorated in 2003 & 6. There are fitted carpets throughout except for the sitting room which has a boarded floor. The kitchen and ground floor corridor have vinyl tiles. Some double glazing. Gas central heating. Access up a private drive to off track parking. Walled garden, and outhouses with moorland behind. Fine for dogs. The nearest beach is 150 metres away down a steep cliff path. Beaches of St Ives bay about 3/4 mile.

Sleeps 9

Forgotten Houses Ltd
01326 340153 www.forgottenhouses.co.uk

Pencobben

Godrevy Point St Ives Bay 31

Pencobben is on the north coast at Godrevy Point, the east end of the sands of St Ives Bay. The sea is not far over the brow of the hill on three sides. This is an unspoilt stretch of coast, famous for its flowers and wild life. Close by are the sandy beaches of Hayle and Godrevy. There is also a quiet sand and rock beach under the cliff a short walk to the east. It is fine for walkers and for family holidays. For those interested in history this is an astonishing area close to one of the oldest Christian sites. The house was built on the site of a farmhouse and was designed as an isolated holiday house in a terrific location, looking over open country. The surroundings and views from the windows (particularly the first floor living room) are spectacular. Pencobben is up a drive from the road, & surrounded by the owners'

100 acres of towans, pasture and dunes. Beyond that is the land of the headland, given by them to the National Trust. There is an enclosed garden on each side and that on the east is within high walls which provide safe and sheltered play for small children. The garden includes a granite monolith of uncertain purpose. The nearest country pub is about a mile away. A couple of miles further on, Hayle has lots of other facilities including shops. Although the house is designed for family holidays, it provides complete peace and quiet, works well (and is warm) for a couple or two with their dog.

This is a wonderful sunny location, on a dramatic headland with great cliffs and miles of beaches for sand, swimming or surfing, yet in a private and isolated position.

Forgotten Houses Ltd
01326 340153 www.forgottenhouses.co.uk

Trevoyan

St Merryn 38

After a stone porch, the front door leads to a stone flagged passage with the kitchen to the left and a sitting room on the right. The back door leads to lawn running round three sides of the house. The large sitting room on the south west corner includes a large table and baby grand piano. There is a second sitting room with open fire, and a fireplace in the breakfast area.

Up the 18th century dog-leg stair, Trevoyan has five bedrooms sleeping 11, one bathroom with bath and a second room with shower but no bath. One of the bedrooms has a large four poster with orthopaedic mattress. T.V.s are in the east sitting room and in the bedroom above. The kitchen has modern units, a fitted electric double oven and hob, microwave, dishwasher, a breakfast area and a second snug to one side. There is a coal operated Rayburn stove for extra cooking and heating. There are also electric radiators, storage heaters and a gas radiator. Upstairs, the floors are mostly fully carpeted. Downstairs, and elsewhere, there are rugs and carpets. The separate utility has washing machine, tumble drier, deep freeze and a stone sink. There is a large garden with lots of lawn, and many extra features, including a wendy house. Private parking. Dogs allowed.

Sleeps 11
If combined with Wreckers and Swallows, each of which has its own garden, can sleep up to 19

Wrecker's (Trevoyan Cottage)

First floor

Wrecker's (Trevoyan Cottage)

North

Metres
0 1 2 3

Ground floor

Trevoyan

The north coast between Newquay and Padstow is one of the most popular areas of Cornwall and includes dramatic cliffs, rocky coves, sandy beaches (there are seven close by) for children and of course surfing beaches, as well as many wonderful places to visit and things to do. South of Trevose Head, which is between Constantine Bay and Harlyn Bay, Trevoyan is on the road just inland of the coast between Porthcothnan Bay and St Merryn. Trevoyan is a listed farmhouse, with lawns and a gravelled drive from the pair of fine ornamental egg-ball finial granite piers at a gate by the road.

The old mediaeval house is still at the back of the C17th, C18th and late Georgian house built to its front and side. This was then further extended around 1860 to provide a west wing. Further extensions to the rear, a pleasant old stone structure and slate roof provide a good looking and interesting old house, whose interior is charming, if a bit confusing. The north west wing has been renovated as "Wreckers". That wing has two sound proofed doors, which can be opened for those looking to combine the two houses. The house is close to the sea and beaches and has fields on all sides and views to the horizon. Beyond the garden behind the house is a large listed barn, a pond with ducks, and further barns. The older style furniture includes a four-poster bed and a selection of books. The layout and furnishing are comfortable rather than modern, with many old features retained.

Popular with families and children. This is a fine old listed house in the countryside, close to a good selection of beaches, and close to all one could wish for a Cornish holiday.

Carew House

St Day 68

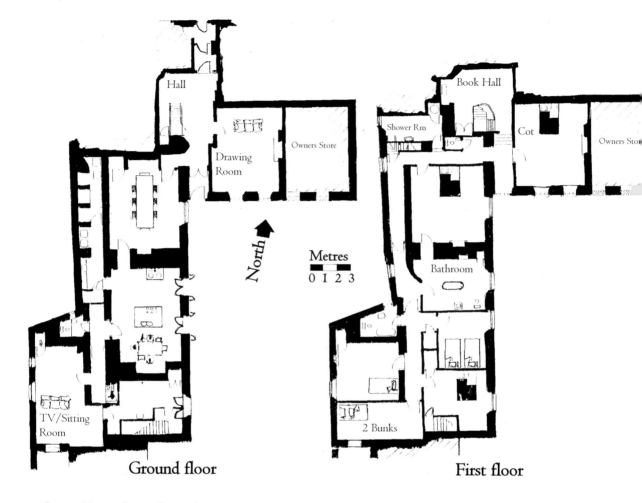

Ground floor

First floor

Carew House has a front door to the village, but normal access is by the rear drive through mature trees and modern housing to the high walled 9000 sq ft garden. The ground floor has planked floors & carpets & main hall, dining room, drawing room, family sitting room, rear hall, utility & large kitchen/breakfast room. The kitchen has slated island unit, double sink, dishwasher, large gas cooker, fridge freezer, microwave, oil fired new blue Aga. The floor is of slate flags. French windows to garden. The rear utility has sink, washing machine, drier, freezer & 2nd fridge freezer. The main drawing room has open fire, shutters (not curtains), CD player. The family sitting room has TV, video, DVD, stereo system. Plenty of space, chairs & sofas. Upstairs are 6 bedrooms, of which one has 2 bunks, & three have double beds. Main bathroom has central roll top bath. There are 2 other shower/bathrooms and 2 other WCs.

The cellar and attic are reserved for owners' stores. General level of furnishing is good with fine decor, interesting decoration and detail and comfortable good furniture. Oil fired central heating. Large private walled garden. Barbecue & garden furniture. Dogs allowed.

Sleeps 10 & cot

Forgotten Houses Ltd
01326 340153 www.forgottenhouses.co.uk

Carew House

St Day 68

Carew House is a large listed Regency house, whose front door looks like that of a small cottage. The house is built in an L shape behind the cottage on the street, with fluted half columns along the garden front. The house of stone was greatly rebuilt by a merchant of 1800 who wished to keep his roots in the pretty village of St Day.

St Day is a little known by-passed village with a family pub, mediaeval cross, market place, clock tower and some 40 listed buildings. It is east of Redruth, and only 5 miles from beaches at Portreath and Porthtowan with its famous Blue bar and golden sands. Chapel Porth is equally beautiful.

Inland it is possible to walk or cycle along the routes of the mineral tramways. The village, once on a mediaeval pilgrim route, was briefly famous before 1840, but seems to have been little visited since. Carew House is like the tardis - bigger inside. The owners bought it as four or five flats, but they have taken out the flimsy partitions and restored it as a fine country house with the original features including shutters, good plasterwork, cornices, doors and other architectural detail.

The layout reflects an unusual history but it is full of interesting things collected by the owners over the years, including a large gong in the hall. Much time and money has been spent on making this a fine family home.

This lovely family house is in a little known but really interesting area with every holiday facility. Our visitors have loved it.

Forgotten Houses Ltd

01326 340153 www.forgottenhouses.co.uk

Pennant Farmhouse

Port Isaac, North Cornwall 58

Pennant Farmhouse is down a long drive and has a disused farm yard behind the house and a large walled garden to the south. The conservatory style porch leads to a large hall with slate flags, an old harmonium and a small pool table. To the left is the carpeted second sitting room, with TV and old granite fireplace. To the right of the hall is a large sitting room with planked floors, big fireplace, wood burning stove, TV, satellite dish, DVD, video & stereo system. An arch at the back of the hall leads to a kitchen about 37 ft long with dining table to one end. The kitchen has new work units (2004), & is well equipped including all new equipment, crockery & so on, 4 ring electric cooker, single oven with grill, oil fired four oven Aga with warming ovens, dishwasher, microwave, fridge. The slate floor has modern planking to the kitchen end. The adjoining utility has two further fridges, washing machine & drier. An old back stair leads from the kitchen to the bedrooms. The back door has a porch and small rear yard with a building where the owners live. Upstairs, a long corridor has five bedrooms and three bathrooms (including shower room).

There is one large double room, a second double room, two rooms with bunks, another with twin beds, and the last has three single beds and a pullout bed. All bathrooms were new 2004. All upstairs rooms carpeted in single colour. The house has double glazing, thick granite walls, and much exposed stone work. Out of sight to the east of the house is the working farm, which includes some residential caravans.

The large garden, which faces south, is neat and tidy with interesting trees & shrubs, large patio area, brick built barbecue, garden seats & benches, and has stone walls to two sides. Dogs allowed. **Sleeps 12**

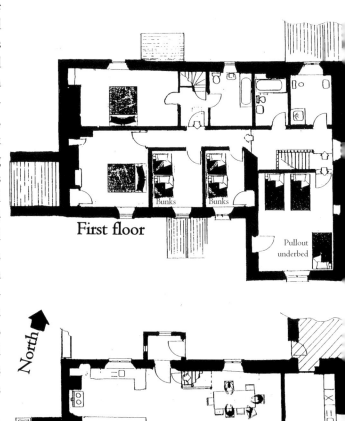

First floor

Bunks

Bunks

Pullout underbed

North

Ground floor

0 1 2 3
Metres

Pennant Farmhouse

Port Isaac, North Cornwall 58

Pennant Farmhouse is about a mile south of Port Isaac on the road from St Endellion. As you come down the drive, there are stunning views of Port Isaac, the north coast and the fields around the farm. This farmhouse, is largely the 1760s rebuild of a smaller cottage. That rebuild used much carved stone from an earlier Tudor mansion and much of this old stonework can be seen around the house, which is built of walls over two feet thick. The roof has a 15th century ridge tile. The high east chimney of double-diamond pattern is unusual for this area.

The farmhouse is still the heart of a working farm which has been in the same family for generations, and whose owners are happy to show visitors around the farm or point out some of the many fine walks. The site is good, conven-ient and only a mile or two east of the beaches at Polzeath. The farmyard to the rear is no longer used, and the fine traditional stone buildings, which are some way to the north, will be slowly renovated. This is a large farmhouse in a good position. Port Isaac is well known, and is so pret-ty that it and the surrounding countryside are used for many TV and film productions.

Although the area has many pubs and restaurants, other good less well-known places are only two or three miles away. And of course there are Polzeath and Rock three miles to the west. To the northwest is much National Trust land, with hidden sandy coves, cliff walks and rocky pool beaches. Pennant Farmhouse has been comfortably renovated and re-equipped to provide a fine fami-ly holiday home, in the best of areas.

Forgotten Houses Ltd

01326 340153   www.forgottenhouses.co.uk

Tresillian House

Manorbier Castle

Forgotten Houses Ltd
01326 340153   www.forgottenhouses.co.uk

Le Sabotier,
Dordogne

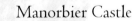

Vicinato, Tuscany

Manorbier Castle

Forgotten Houses Ltd
01326 340153 www.forgottenhouses.co.uk

Tresillian House

Newquay 40

The house was redecorated and renovated in 2001, 2004 and completely refitted again in 2007. The main south porch leads to the first entrance hall and then to a full height stair hall with an oak open well grand stair (curious newels) & balustraded balcony beneath an octagonal cupola. The ground floor includes a fine library, with original shelving and loads of books, a glorious large south facing drawing room, a large dining room and a kitchen. The main reception rooms have moulded plaster cornices. The house has central heating. The library, hall, dining and drawing rooms have original fireplaces, grates, surrounds and tiles and the drawing room has a Carrara marble fireplace. The furniture, furnishings and curtains are of good quality and comfortable with matching sofas and a big ottoman and chairs in the drawing room. TV and video. The dining room table seats 12. Ground floors are sanded with carpet or scatter rugs, or tiled; upstairs has plain light carpet throughout.

There are nine bedrooms. Two have magnificent four posters, and another a pair of bunks. There are six bathrooms one of which has a marble bath. Two have unusual layouts & fine ball & claw roll top baths. Two have showers over the bath, one bathroom has shower only. Downstairs W.C. Kitchen has a four oven oil fired Aga, electric hob, microwave, dishwasher, cafetiere, fridge/freezer and small breakfast table by the window seats. High chair. The utility room has commercial sized washing machine and drier. Large gardens (including small lake about 80 yards from house. Large climbing frame. The renovation of service outbuildings some distance away has provided a further astonishing wing with many facilities which may also be available Because this is a large house to get ready, arrival is only after 4.00pm. **No dogs. Sleeps 15 & cot**

First floor

Ground floor

Bunks

Future kitchen

Owners store

Metres

0 1 2 3

North

A new kitchen and breakfast room is to be fitted out in the old kitchens at the end of 2007

Forgotten Houses Ltd
01326 340153   www.forgottenhouses.co.uk

Tresillian House

On the site of an older mansion, Tresillian was rebuilt as a substantial country house around 1801, then rebuilt and extended in 1848. The house stands in 200 acres about five miles from the coast at Newquay and is therefore suitable for the holiday activities of both coast and inland.

Tresillian is a large, luxurious Regency house. It is now an 'L' shaped house with private gardens of 22 acres, including terrace, lawns, ornamental lake, fountain and a walled vegetable garden. It has thick walls of gritstone with granite quoins, radial stone heads to the windows, with fine chimneys and a central cupola. The roof has granite and timber corbels beneath a slate roof. You arrive by the north drive at an imposing carriage sweep surrounded by lawns. Part of the rear staff wing is lived in. The home farm now renovated or converted is two hundred yards away.

Completely redecorated and re-carpeted, the house retains many features including shutters, panelling, coffered ceilings, fine doors and fittings, wall mirrors, splendid fireplaces. Other enjoyable features are club fenders and a dinner gong. We think there are 38 windows - of which two are of glazed trompe-l'oeil. Nearly every visitor has had a much enjoyed tour of the grounds from the Head Gardener, famous for his talks on the subject and for moon gardening. Organic vegetables may also be available. The house is meticulously maintained and looked after. There is a large terrace to the west.

This is a fine and stylish house in a good location. It is surrounded by woodland and farmland and only a mile from Trerice. It is close to many attractions, but above all is close to the beaches, swimming and surfing, for which the area is famous.

Manorbier Castle

Pembrokeshire, Wales 60

Once through the outer bailey, you pick up the keys to the great gate of the inner bailey & to the house built against the walls. The entrance is up steps to a large sitting room, looking over the bailey. This room has good quality furniture, high ceilings, and long window seats. TV & video. The open fire can not be used. A flying walkway leads to a room with king sized double bed in the mediaeval gatehouse, with its own shower room and a WC in the thickness of old walls. At the other end of the sitting room are two pretty, newly redecorated bedrooms, and two new bathrooms, one en suite. One has twin beds, the other a double bed. Stairs go up to an attic twin bedded room or down to the dining room, with a fine table (seats 12).

Second floor

Principal floor

Entrance

North

Metres
0 1 2 3

Ground floor

Chalet: Built within walled garden

French windows lead to a private high walled garden with the chalet placed within high walls at the end. The chalet has twin beds, bunks, and shower room. Although with electric heating - the chalet is not up to the standard of the main house. The kitchen has vinyl floor, modern units, & breakfast table. Electric range style cooker, microwave, 2 fridges, freezer, dishwasher. The utility has sink, washing machine, drier. Garden WC.

Oil fired central heating.

Patio area & garden furniture. Since there are walls and towers, children should be supervised outside the house. Cot & high chair available. Private catering possible. Dogs allowed out of season. The house & garden make a fascinating and private retreat within the great castle, hidden from seasonal castle visitors.

Friday Changeover   Sleeps 12 & cot

Forgotten Houses Ltd
01326 340153 www.forgottenhouses.co.uk

Manorbier Castle

Pembrokeshire, Wales   60

Manorbier is a mediaeval walled castle, some 900 years old. One of few private castles available for letting, it is at the mouth of a wild valley by the sea in Pembrokeshire, Wales. Across the way is the isolated old church and beyond the outer bailey is the village. This has a shop and the Castle Arms pub with fire and good beer. A nearby small hotel has a good restaurant. This magnificent section of coast has cliff walks and a sandy beach a hundred yards below the castle. The seaside town of Tenby is a few miles east, and Pembroke a few miles west. There is a lot to see and do in the area, but most will want to spend as much time as possible in the castle.

Many books have been written on Manorbier and there are many websites full of pictures. Perhaps the most succinct comment is from the 12th century: "The most pleasant place in all the broadlands of Wales." It really is difficult to know where to start. This is a big place and building. Although it is open during the day to visitors from Easter to September, the house and garden are private. The inner bailey has flowers and shrub beds against the old vaulted chapel, keep, towers and well preserved walls. The house is partly within 12th century rooms and partly on and of old structures altered in the 17th and 19th centuries, and so is of different levels, with its own courtyard garden.

There is nothing quite like shutting yourself in the whole castle, wandering amongst the walls, climbing the towers and knowing you have the whole place to yourself. Manorbier is romantic, fascinating and beautiful.

This has long been an admired and unique holiday house. Now further improved, it must be one of the most exceptional and wonderful places to stay in all Britain.

Forgotten Houses Ltd
01326 340153   www.forgottenhouses.co.uk

Le Sabotier

Montcuq, France 19

Le Sabotier was renovated some years ago for its English owner. The main floor has sitting room with dining area & the kitchen beyond. Upstairs the gallery bedroom has four-poster bed and its own bathroom. A staircase (2005) goes down to the lower floor which has a double bed and two singles in one room and then a shower room (2006) with basin & WC.

The sitting room is entered off steep steps from the tiny street, opposite the church. It has a wood-burning stove which will take the chill off the evenings in spring and autumn and provide a good central heat all day in the winter. There is DVD and TV. (French channels only). Logs for the woodburner are extra. Central heating added for 2007.

The kitchen, designed in Provencal fashion with wood shelves and cupboards in blue and yellow and fabrics to match, is equipped with a gas cooker, microwave, fridge, washing machine, dishwasher, food processor and cafetiere. The kitchen door leads onto the terrace and barbecue area with table and chairs partly shaded by a fig tree and vine.

Across the lane is a larger garden ideal for sun lounging with its SW aspect, and next to it the private pool shared with La Maison Volets Rouges. The pool is 10 metres x 5.5 metres with a depth of between 1.0 and 1.5 metres. There are terrific views across the valley.

Sleeps 4 to 6

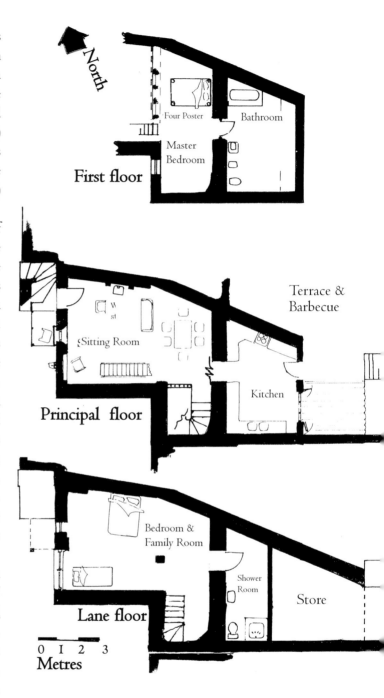

North

First floor

Four Poster

Bathroom

Master Bedroom

Terrace & Barbecue

Sitting Room

W st

Principal floor

Kitchen

Bedroom & Family Room

Shower Room

Store

Lane floor

0 1 2 3
Metres

Le Sabotier

Montcuq, France 19

Les Volets Rouges, next door to Le Sabotier, sleeps 8 to 10, and may be available. Together, the two houses sleep 14. Plans, photos & details are available.

South of the Dordogne, in the Lot, is a country rich in castles, fortified hill towns, caves, gorges and rolling agricultural land. Although becoming better appreciated, this is a less well-known area of tiny roads, farm hamlets and sun - lots of sun. The countryside has sunflowers, corn, lavender, vines, good wines and local delicacies. There are many restaurants. Montcuq has a 12th century tower, Sunday market, small shops, cafes, tennis courts, an open air swimming pool and a man made sandy beach and big swimming lake. The oldest dwellings were in the cliff behind the village, but Lebreil is now a south facing hamlet of 14 houses (& a mayor) about two miles from Montcuq. Le Sabotier is in the middle of a tiny steep mediaeval street, opposite the church. The house is on three levels with a terrace on the south-east, shaded by a fig tree and mature vine, with barbecue, among the variegated russet coloured pantile roofs. Inside, the shape of the building reflects its age and chaotic building history. The walls are bare stone, the ceiling high; there is space, sense of calm and a wood-burning stove. The layout is eccentric. The ground floor, once perhaps for animals and most recently the cobbler's workshop, is now a large second family room. The main rooms are extraordinary and a puzzle of steps and angles. There is another tiny balcony to the west to watch the sun go down over the church. There is a swimming pool across the lane. The English owner lives next door and can help with where to eat, buy wine, swim, shop or visit. Lots of visitors have written unasked to praise their French holidays.

Forgotten Houses Ltd
01326 340153 www.forgottenhouses.co.uk

Vicinato

Garfagnana, Tuscany 32

Vicinato is up a twisting mountain road a couple of miles from the town and about 40 minutes from Pisa airport and ten minutes walk from the hamlet shop. It has four main bedrooms and two reception rooms together with a tiled bathroom which has a shower over the very small bath. Renovation works have included relaying the old pantiled roof, and building a large terrace facing south over the valley. The lowest floor, with sealed stone walls, will provide more rooms and works of improvement continue slowly each winter. Windows have been carefully renewed in chestnut.

Downstairs the floors are solid tile, with rug covered timber boarding in some rooms. The kitchen has a gas cooker and its own breakfast table. There is a washing machine. The larger of the two sitting rooms has a big fireplace. Although the facilities and decoration are basic, these details and description may not be up to date with all improvements. The owner speaks good English. Local help may also be available and the house and grounds are maintained by the family. Only available from May to the end of September. **Sleeps 8**

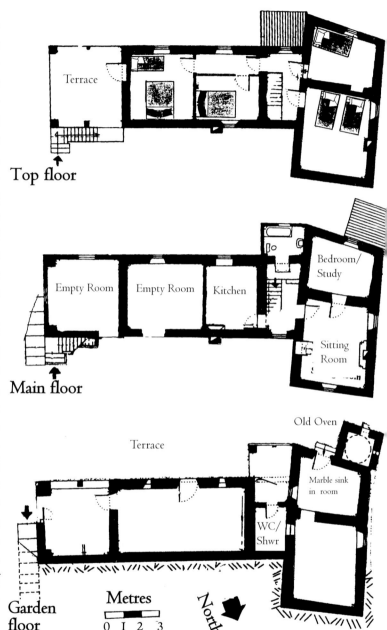

Top floor

Main floor

Garden floor

Metres
0 1 2 3

North

Vicinato

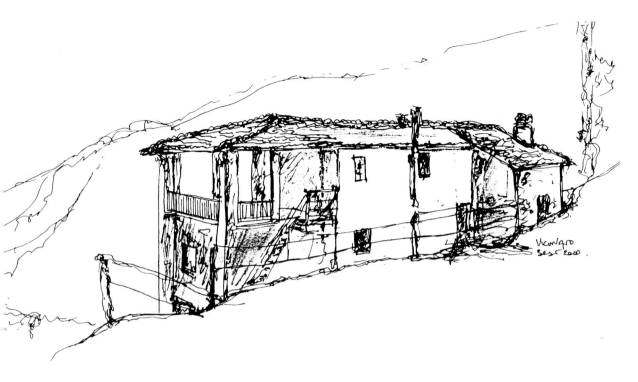

Tuscany, on the western flank of Italy, north of Rome, is one of the most beautiful areas of Europe. Northern Tuscany has castles to the north west, beaches to the west, the towns of Florence and Pisa to the south, with many other smaller towns of mediaeval and Renaissance architecture. North of Lucca, and in the Garfagnana National Park, Vicinato is a farm that has been in the ownership of the same family for about three hundred years.

Built against the hillside in the 18th century, & largely of stone, the lower floor includes an enormous oven and storage. You live on the upper two floors reached directly from the hillside. The house has wonderful views of the mountains and vineyards, and a covered terrace is the perfect spot to sip wine and admire the vineyards, olives and fruit trees, through which you are welcome to wander. The house has been let by us for some years and we have had some appreciative letters about holidays and the restaurants and sights of the area. There is an all purpose shop and bar within walking distance and a large public swimming pool in the village at the bottom of the twisting road.

The villages and towns of the area are charming. The nearby village of Molazzana has an all purpose shop, church, alleyways and square. You need a car to travel the area. Then you may visit Barga with its museum, markets, pool and shops, wonderful Lucca, or Pisa, Florence, the small towns of Northern Tuscany with their Mediaeval architecture- or even the seaside which is just over an hour away. Most of our visitors have wanted to return and one or two have claimed the house has given them the best holiday ever. This is a fine old farmhouse in basic Forgotten Houses style, in a beautiful area.

Forgotten Houses Ltd
01326 340153   www.forgottenhouses.co.uk

Our Visitors' Comments...

All houses have visitors' books. Entries are always appreciated and respected. Most visitors write something, and many write at length. This selection cannot attempt to include notes from every house, or reflect the length of some diary entries, views and recommendations. However, we have visited each of the houses and will be happy to tell you more.

"Beautifully restored cottage and a fireplace that takes 6 foot logs (has now been burning continuously for 6½ days)"

"Why **Mellinzeath** you ask ? ... to return to the roots and get back to basics. ... what a stay... calm, quiet misty mornings, stoking fires and tasty dinners - what more could you ask for."

"It has been a real pleasure to stay in such a beautiful setting."

"A wonderful place to stay and calm down. The long journey (over 15 hours by car) was well worth it. Thanks for a lovely week at **Boconnoc**" ... Visitors from Switzerland.

"It is with great sadness that we drag ourselves away from this idyllic location - a week simply hasn't been long enough. The grounds are so lovely and a highlight of our stay was a walk at twilight to see the deer." (**Grooms**)

"A fantastic place.....Wonderful setting.. Amazing cottage ...peace and quiet and constant hot water." (**Little Bosvarren**)

"Lovely cottage and the walks are stunning - lanes are magical with banks clothed in a mossy patchwork - smells are so good - we'll be back!" (**Little Bosvarren**)
"We had a very enjoyable fortnight here, despite many of our sight seeing plans being forestalled by sheer laziness ... we spent several days just basking in the sun in the walled garden, quaffing wine and watching the lizards. Such days often ended with a leisurely barbecue." (**Le Sabotier**)

"Lovely house which exceeded our expectations. Views from the terrace garden enjoyed over many glasses of wine. Very relaxing holiday, it's a shame to have to go home." (**Le Sabotier**)

"We have had a lovely week, visited some great places and stayed in this beautiful cottage. We had some great days out at St. Ives, Fowey, Padstow and Mevagissey. Stunning scenery, enjoyable walks and beautiful beaches." (**Colomiar**)

"A very lucky start to the year. A cancellation meant we were able to experience the delights of **Colomiar**. May our good fortune continue."

"We have wished for nothing, except that we had booked a second week." (**Polwartha**)

"For the third year running, we had a terrific time.. Coverack fantastic...Kynance Cove has a water tunnel formed by two rocks, which the children loved." (**The Lodge**)

"Having been to Cornwall many times we can honestly say that **Badgers** is the loveliest cottage we have stayed in."

"Have not seen any badgers this year, just the odd unicorn but it was a full moon and the wine was good !!"

"A lovely cottage - we enjoyed the attention to detail and the warmth and comfort it provided - Peace, perfect peace."

"We thought **Bosbenna** was excellent in every respect and the best accommodation we have occupied in Cornwall. In an age when people tend to complain continually about almost anything, you should be congratulated on providing such excellent standards. Keep it up."

"A beautiful house in a spectacular location."

"Both **Trevoyan** and **Wreckers** were a delight. We felt very welcome. Hope to return soon."

"Great house and great location. The kids had a fantastic time". (**Trevoyan**)

"**Wreckers** has been restored beautifully. We have been very comfortable and thoroughly enjoyed our holiday and made to feel welcome."

Our Visitors' Comments...

"The house, (tastefully converted), location, & Cornwall did more than match expectations.."

"Very comfortable well organised house - not too done over and safe for small children."

"Another excellent meal...the holiday for us all in two lovely relaxing weeks."

"The house and location were just as I imagined- a fairy tale dream"

"Deserted sandy beach down a track off the road to Gunwalloe.. delightful countryside."

"I liked the fudge shop in Fowey"

" A delightful cottage in perfect position & we will warmly recommend it."

"Over the years, we have stayed in some lovely houses, but none to match **Little Pinnock**"

"Activities included hiring a motor boat. The children loved it."

"Can't believe we go home tomorrow, the time has sped past. Went riding again on Skippy .. had a final sail in Mylor harbour"

"A wonderful little house every bit as beautiful as the brochure suggested. We tried out the hip bath. The beds were wonderfully warm and cosy.."

"Absolutely fantastic......best holiday we've ever had...better than basic." (**Vicinato**)

"A lovely house in a quiet setting". "How much the five of us enjoyed the complete tranquillity of this place & how homely we found it." (**Higher Bosvarren**)

"I have just returned from a cottage that was faultless in every major respect."

"...Good pubs... Good beaches... Good walks..."

"Lovely countryside, coast and beaches. Who needs abroad?"

" Enjoy yourselves. We did"

"Lovely Holiday. We will be back"

"Thank you for a wonderful holiday at **Lower Bosvarren**, ideal situation and place to stay. We wished we could afford 2 weeks instead of one!"

"Wonderful, romantic, rural setting, great architecture, lovely exterior and interior structural features."

"We have thoroughly enjoyed living in this lovely old property with the surrounding gardens and lawns, ideal for 3 teenaged boys to play football etc."

"A beautiful peaceful cottage in a fantastic area" (**Higher Bosvarren**)

"Lovely roomy farmhouse. Very clean and welcoming and comfortable beds. We enjoyed playing cricket and football in the garden."

"Have had a lovely week in Cornwall, so much to do so little time. The house is lovely with great character. The setting is great and enjoyed walks around the farm, will come again."

"The house was beautiful, full of charm and character, particularly the fact that it was a proper long house. The floor of the table tennis room was a great archaeological talking point."

"The house is in an idyllic position, very child friendly."

"If you have dogs then this is the place to come."

"We have had the most idyllic week at **Little Bosvarren**. We spent days enjoying the peace and quiet of this lovely location. The house has everything we need and enough space for us to completely unwind."

"The cottage was very comfortable and cosy. The space in the cottage allowed us to have relatives to visit. Will return for more of the same."

"We love this place; it is so peaceful and private. The cottage is comfortable and well equipped. I shall definitely use **Forgotten Houses** again and have already recommended it to friends."

"Such a beautiful cottage. Very safe and fun for our son aged 3, he has enjoyed staying here, which is the best compliment we can give."

Forgotten Houses Ltd
01326 340153 www.forgottenhouses.co.uk

Our Visitors' Comments...

"This is our third **Forgotten Houses** experience, another wonderful holiday."

"Another great holiday here. Very comfortable, great Kitchen. Nice to have somewhere for doggie too."(**Bosbenna**)

"An absolutely gorgeous place. Looking forward to coming back"

"A gem of a cottage, spacious, cosy and roomy."
"What a wonderful place to spend Thanksgiving, we would highly recommend it."

"An amazing property in a superb location, a perfect base for a Cornish holiday."

"Great house, great holiday I could live here forever."

"Lovely spacious house, plenty to see and do within an hours drive."

"Without a doubt one of the finest weeks of our life! We have fallen in love with **Bosbenna** and don't want to leave."

"We are really glad to have found '**Forgotten Houses**' on the Internet - for us they are no longer Forgotten."(**Bosvathick Lodge**)

"Our third stay at **The Lodge**"

"The cottage was really cute and cosy and we loved the big garden and tree house"

"We all enjoyed our stay at **The Lodge**, a unique and restful experience"

"Lovely surrounding countryside - great for walking."

"Wonderful week, such a restful place. Spent time walking and exploring the area but also a lot of time relaxing and enjoying the tranquillity of '**Littleworth**' - we would love to come back."

"Such a surprise to find somewhere that exceeds your expectations - such a lovely place inside and out. Have had a great time."

"The house is situated in a beautiful location and is very well kept." (**Wreckers**)

"Beautiful cottage, which is really spacious in a great position. Amazing fireplace."

"Fantastic week - great home, weather and beaches. House was unique, cosy and had everything we needed. The animals were an added bonus."

"Really fun cottage - we were made to feel really welcome."

"Very homely - the animals were a bonus - thank you."
"Great house - lots of space." (**Trevoyan**)

"Lovely setting - relaxing house."

"Great holiday, great house, thanks for everything."

"Fantastic week. Hope to see you next year."

"**Trevoyan** and **Wreckers** were a delight. We felt very welcome. Hope to return soon."

"The house and location is fantastic. The kids had a lovely time."

"We loved the garden for cricket and badminton."

"I have had a lovely time and will miss it. I wish I lived here too."

"We have all had a wonderful time and were made very welcome. Hope to see you again." (**Le Sabotier**)

"Everything has been fantastic - the house is all we could wish for - very well equipped and comfortable. Our mistake was not coming for 2 weeks!"

"Lovely house, lovely place, lovely people - thanks for making our stay memorable and welcoming. Rest assured we will be back for more."

"Thank you for our stay in your quiet retreat. We had a great time; not enough time."

"Views from the terrace garden enjoyed over many glasses of wine. Very relaxing holiday."

"We were stunned by the quality of the accommodation and we had a fantastic time. We day tripped but it was so nice in the house that we stayed there for the most part. Thanks again and we will be contacting you shortly to book our next holiday." (**Carew House**)

Our Visitors' Comments...

"Calm, quiet misty mornings. Back to basics. We had many a nice walk and the locals are friendly." (**Mellinzeath**)

"Have enjoyed every minute spent here, the silence only interrupted by mooing!"

"A very pretty, peaceful location for our honeymoon."

"The cottage and location were just as I imagined - a fairy tale dream."

"We wanted seclusion and this location certainly gave us that and more. With 2 dogs the woods have been ideal with no fear of them coming to any harm"

"A wonderful place to stay and calm down." (**Grooms**)

"What a wonderful place - superb accommodation, wonderful surroundings. We particularly enjoyed walking and cycling around the estate. Nice and safe for the children

"A perfect house and location to re-charge the batteries."

"Thank you for making us so welcome during our stay"

"We have had a lovely week. Stunning scenery, enjoyable walks and beautiful beaches - a beautiful cottage." (**Colomiar**)

"Lovely house, location and aspect"

"We would recommend this cottage to everyone but especially to tall people and musicians, as it boasts an impressive entrance and minstrels gallery."

"Our second visit here and even better this time! Inside a well thought out conversion. We have been cocooned in the warmth of the log fire."

"We have been renting cottages for over 30 years and yours was definitely one of the best"

"We have wished for nothing except that we had booked a second week" (**Polwartha**)

"We've had a lovely week here at Polwartha and the surrounding countryside is just beautiful."
"Superb views, quiet, unspoilt nature - please do nothing to change this, spots like this are now almost impossible to find."

"Very nice, like the Aga, very central and safe for dogs"

"Having been to Cornwall many times we can honestly say that Badgers is the loveliest cottage we have stayed in." (**Badgers**)

"A lovely cottage - we enjoyed the attention to detail and warmth and comfort it provided."

"Our dog has thoroughly enjoyed her holiday"

We found **Josiah's** utterly charming in every way and it provided all we could have wanted for a happy holiday, having been sympathetically and well restored, we found it both cheerful and comfortable.

Finally, we were very pleased with this note by LL:
"I love the FH website- and the houses live up to the promise".

Forgotten Houses Ltd
01326 340153 www.forgottenhouses.co.uk

Booking Terms and Conditions

1. Forgotten Houses is a trading name of Forgotten Houses Ltd ('the company') whose registered office is at Bosvathick Constantine Falmouth TR11 5RD, who act entirely and only as booking agents for the owners ("the owner") of all the properties offered. Contracts accepted by the company shall be between the person signing the application form ("the tenant") and the owner of the property whose name is shown on the company's form of acceptance.

2. The tenancy confers upon the tenant the right to occupy for a holiday. Unless so agreed in writing, bookings cannot be accepted from groups of single persons under the age of 25, or all male or female parties with more than two persons.

3. Lettings are for a maximum of four weeks and, unless otherwise agreed in writing, or so specified in the details for a particular house, commence at 3.00pm on the first day of the let, ending at 10.00am on the day of departure, allowing time for cleaning of the property between visitors. Lettings generally commence on a Saturday afternoon and finish on the Saturday morning, except for a weekend, midweek or other agreed period.

4. The company holds a telephone booking for four working days, until a booking form and a deposit equal to thirty percent of the full rent due is received. If the booking is not accepted, the deposit will be refunded in full.

5. Once a booking is accepted by the company as agents, a contract for the occupation has been agreed, and the balance due is payable eight weeks before the start of the tenancy, for which no reminder is necessarily sent. Bookings made within eight weeks of occupation require that payment in full be made at the time of booking. If any payment due in relation to your booking is not received by the due date, the company on behalf of the owner is entitled to treat the tenant's booking as cancelled and the company may immediately attempt to remarket the property in order, on behalf of the owner, to use best efforts to minimise the loss for the tenant.

6. A cancellation by the tenant after acceptance by the company of a booking constitutes a breach of contract. Due to the period of time that is usual between booking and occupation, the owner may have turned away other prospective tenants in the period between acceptance and cancellation, and thereafter be unable to obtain a booking, despite the owner's best endeavours to minimise the tenant's loss, including the use of advertising and making of special offers. In the case of cancellation by the tenant, the owner shall be entitled to retain any sum paid as a deposit and may also bring a claim against the person signing the booking form for a sum equal to the owner's additional losses, if any, including loss of profit, suffered by reason of the cancellation.

Non-payment of the outstanding balance of monies due eight weeks prior to the start of the tenancy shall be deemed a cancellation. It is emphasized that reasonable and proper cancellation charges may be as much as the total cost of the holiday booking. However, rents cannot be taken for a property twice, and the company will use every effort to relet a property if told in writing that the tenant wishes to change the date, or no longer requires the property. If and when a property is relet, credit will be given for the full replacement rent obtained and received, less any deposit paid together with reasonable costs of additional advertising and letting, if any, if and when the cancelled period is re-let to third parties, and funds received.

7. The tenant agrees:

a) To arrive at the property before 8.00pm on the day the tenancy commences, in order to assure the security of the property, unless an alternative arrangement is agreed in writing with the company. Failure to arrive without prior agreement before 12pm the day after the tenancy commences, will be regarded as cancellation, and no refund of any monies paid by the tenant will be made.

b) To take good care of the property and contents and to leave it in a clean and tidy condition. No cleaning service is provided in the course of the tenancy. The tenant is responsible to the owner for the actual costs of any breakage or damage in or to the property, along with any additional costs that may result, which are caused by the tenant or any member of the tenant's party, and the owner can require payment from the tenant to cover any such costs.

c) To permit the owners and their agents reasonable access to the property.

d) Not to part with possession of the property, or share it save with members of the party shown on the booking form, and not to exceed the number of people shown in the property description.

e) Not to allow a pet into the property unless first notified to and then agreed to by the company.

Pets are not allowed on chairs or beds, and are never to be left unattended in the property

8. Electricity, fuel, wood, gas and oil are supplied as appropriate & without further charge for use on the property unless specifically mentioned as an extra in the rate chart.

9. Pets are allowed, where so permitted in writing, when a weekly charge is made for each pet.

10. Use of the home and any amenities provided to the applicant are provided by owners to the applicants entirely at user's risk, and no responsibility can be accepted for loss or damage to any persons or persons' property who use the property.

11. As noted in the handbook descriptions and other literature of the company, the details include scale plans noting furniture on a representational basis only and there may also have been improvements, renovation, alterations or changes in detail, layout, furniture and equipment between the date of publication and the date of the holiday. The company makes reasonable efforts to ensure that the information given in relation to a property is accurate and complete when so given. In case of any discrepancy between these booking conditions and the contents of any handbook or correspondence, these conditions prevail.

12. If for any reason beyond the owner's control the property is not available on the date booked (due to fire damage, for example) or the property is unavailable for holiday letting, all rents and charges paid in advance by the tenant will be refunded in full.

13. All or any complaints must be notified to the company immediately so that the owners or their agents can make an immediate on the site investigation and, if necessary, take remedial action. If complaints are raised after the tenancy the owners or the company as agents for the owners will have been denied the opportunity to investigate and endeavour to put right any such matter, during the tenancy.

14. If there shall be any material breach of these conditions including, but not limited to, vandalism or disturbance, the owners or their agents reserve the right to re-enter the property and terminate the tenancy without prejudice to the other rights and remedies of the owners.

15. The contract is deemed to have been made at Bosvathick, Constantine, Falmouth, Cornwall, and the proper law of the contract is English.

16. The person signing the booking form must be a member of the party intending to occupy, be over eighteen years old, and certify that he or she is authorised to agree the booking conditions on behalf of all persons included on the booking form, including those he or she may substitute or add at a later date.

Forgotten Houses Ltd
01326 340153 www.forgottenhouses.co.uk